D0295179

ARITHMETIC

This book is written for those who wish to gain a practical working knowledge of arithmetic. It differs from the majority of arithmetic textbooks in that it explains in unusual detail the actual processes involved in the various kinds of arithmetical calculation. Whereas most books contain the minimum amount of expository matter and concentrate on the orderly assembly of graded examples for working, this book makes exposition a primary aim, while also providing the numerous examples which the student must have if he is to confirm what he has learnt.

"In this new addition to the well-known series, a wide field of topics in general arithmetic is covered very efficiently and skilfully. The difficulties likely to face a student working by himself are always kept in view. Explanations are full and illustrated by many worked examples, in such a way as to maintain the student's interest. The exercises to be worked by the student consist of well-chosen examples and are of reasonable length, considering the size of the book. It can be recommended to all students wishing to improve their basic arithmetic."

Technical Journal

TEACH YOURSELF BOOKS

ARITHMETIC

L. C. PASCOE, M.A.

Headmaster, Ducie Technical High School for Boys,
Manchester
Sometime Baring Open Scholar in Mathematics,
Hertford College, Oxford

TEACH YOURSELF BOOKS

ST PAUL'S HOUSE   WARWICK LANE   LONDON EC4

First printed 1958
This impression 1970

ISBN 0 340 05512 X

PRINTED AND BOUND IN ENGLAND
FOR THE ENGLISH UNIVERSITIES PRESS LTD
BY HAZELL WATSON AND VINEY LTD, AYLESBURY

INTRODUCTION

This book is written for those who wish to gain a practical working knowledge of arithmetic, and particularly for those who wish to do so without the guidance of a teacher. As a "Teach Yourself" book, it differs from the majority of arithmetic text-books in that it explains in unusual detail the actual processes involved in the various kinds of arithmetical calculation. Whereas most books contain the minimum amount of expository matter and concentrate on the orderly assembly of graded examples for working, this book makes exposition a primary aim, while also providing the numerous examples which the student must have if he is to confirm what he has learnt.

The subject is developed comprehensively from its beginnings, the elementary processes being dealt with in the first nine chapters. Chapter 10, on arithmetical graphs, includes a very short account of statistical applications. There then follow three chapters of a practical nature which should be of use as an elementary basis for engineering and allied courses. Chapters 14–16 are devoted to Civil Arithmetic, and it is hoped that these will prove of help to almost all those who have any source of income: some of the simpler aspects of Income Tax and insurance are explained in a straightforward manner, together with the details of Stock Exchange procedure. The last chapter serves as an introduction to the arithmetical background of certain kinds of electronic computing machine, which are now becoming so important. References are made here and there to other works which can be used as aids to further study.

The author wishes to express his gratitude to Mr. E. A. Side (who has read the entire manuscript), for his invaluable suggestions; to Mr. W. L. Elmes, who read the section on Income Tax; and to Mr. C. J. Pike for his help on Insurance. Acknowledgement is made to the Chislehurst and Sidcup Urban District Council for permission to reprint a part of their General Rate Demand Note, and to Messrs. Elliott Bros (London) for the kind assistance of their Computing Division. The encouragement and suggestions of Mr. E. S. Jenkins and Mr. J. H. Walsh have been invaluable, and finally grateful thanks are due to Mr. Leonard Cutts and the English Universities Press for their unfailing courtesy and assistance during the preparation of this work.

L. C. PASCOE

North Cray, Sidcup

CONTENTS

CHAPTER 1

THE BIRTH OF ARITHMETIC

CHAPTER 2

ARITHMETIC—THE FOUR RULES

CHAPTER 3

FACTORS

CHAPTER 4

FRACTIONS

CHAPTER 5

MONEY

CHAPTER 6

WEIGHTS AND MEASURES

CHAPTER 7

DECIMALS—THE METRIC SYSTEM

CHAPTER 8

RATIO, PROPORTION, AVERAGES

CHAPTER 9

PERCENTAGE, PROFIT AND LOSS

CHAPTER 10

ARITHMETICAL GRAPHS

CHAPTER 11

MENSURATION OF RECTANGULAR FIGURES

CHAPTER 12

LOGARITHMS

CHAPTER 13

THE CIRCLE, CYLINDER, CONE AND SPHERE

CHAPTER 14

SIMPLE AND COMPOUND INTEREST

CHAPTER 15

RATES, TAXES AND INSURANCE

CHAPTER 16

INVESTMENTS AND THE STOCK EXCHANGE

CHAPTER 17

COMPUTING MACHINES AND THE BINARY SCALE

MULTIPLICATION TABLE

×	1	2	3	4	5	6	7	8	9	10	11	12
1	1	2	3	4	5	6	7	8	9	10	11	12
2	2	4	6	8	10	12	14	16	18	20	22	24
3	3	6	9	12	15	18	21	24	27	30	33	36
4	4	8	12	16	20	24	28	32	36	40	44	48
5	5	10	15	20	25	30	35	40	45	50	55	60
6	6	12	18	24	30	36	42	48	54	60	66	72
7	7	14	21	28	35	42	49	56	63	70	77	84
8	8	16	24	32	40	48	56	64	72	80	88	96
9	9	18	27	36	45	54	63	72	81	90	99	108
10	10	20	30	40	50	60	70	80	90	100	110	120
11	11	22	33	44	55	66	77	88	99	110	121	132
12	12	24	36	48	60	72	84	96	108	120	132	144

Example: $9 \times 6 = 54$

LENGTH

12 inches (in.) = 1 foot (ft.)
3 feet (ft.) = 1 yard (yd.)
5½ yards (yd.) = 1 pole (p.)
40 poles (p.) = 1 furlong (fur.)

22 yards (yd.) = 1 chain (ch.)
10 chains (ch.) = 1 furlong (fur.)
8 furlongs (fur.) = 1 mile (mi.)

From this we have:
220 yd. = 1 fur.
5280 ft. = 1760 yd. = 1 mi.

Surveyors also use:
100 links = 1 chain (ch.)

At sea, the following are used:
6 ft. = 1 fathom
200 yd. = 1 cable
1 knot = 1 nautical mile per hour
= 6080 ft. per hour.

AREA

144 sq. in.	= 1 sq. ft.	40 sq. p.	= 1 rood (r.)
9 sq. ft.	= 1 sq. yd.	4 roods (r.)	= 1 acre (ac.)
30¼ sq. yd.	= 1 sq. pole	640 acres	= 1 sq. mile

From this we have:
4840 sq. yd. = 1 acre

Also:
10 sq. chain = 1 acre

VOLUME

1728 cu. in. = 1 cu. ft.	27 cu. ft.	= 1 cu. yd.

WEIGHT

AVOIRDUPOIS

16 ounces	= 1 pound (lb.) (oz.)
14 lb.	= 1 stone (st.)
28 lb.	= 1 quarter (qr.)
4 qr.	= 1 hundredweight (cwt.)
20 cwt.	= 1 ton (t.)

TROY (precious metals)

24 grains	= 1 pennyweight (gr.) (dwt.)
20 dwt.	= 1 ounce

There used to be a troy pound (of 12 oz. troy). It is now obsolete.

The avoirdupois and troy ounces are different

1 oz. avoirdupois = 437½ grains, 1 oz. troy = 480 grains
the grain being the same in each case.

CAPACITY

4 gills	= 1 pint (pt.)*	4 pecks (pk.)	= 1 bushel (bush.)
2 pints (pt.)	= 1 quart (qt.)		
4 quarts (qt.)	= 1 gallon (gall.)	8 bushels (bush.)	= 1 quarter (qr.)
2 gallons (gall.)	= 1 peck (pk)		

* Note that the table reads: 4, 2, 4, 2, 4, 8.

TIME

60 seconds (sec.)	= 1 minute (min.)	7 days	= 1 week
		14 days	= 1 fortnight
60 minutes (min.)	= 1 hour (hr.)	365 days	= 1 year
		366 days	= 1 leap year
24 hours (hr.)	= 1 day		

Number of Days in Each Month. January 31, February 28/29, March 31, April 30, May 31, June 30, July 31, August 31, September 30, October 31, November 30, December 31.*

A Leap Year is one whose date is divisible by 4, e.g. 1956, 1960, *unless* the date is divisible by 100, but not by 400. For example, 1800 and 1900 were not leap years. 2000 A.D. will be. February has 28 days in an ordinary year, 29 in each leap year.

* The student who is interested in the origins of the Calendar is strongly recommended to read "Romance in Arithmetic" by Margaret E. Bowman, University of London Press.

MONEY

4 farthings (f.)	= 1 penny (d.)	1 half-crown	= 2s. 6d.
12 pence (d.)	= 1 shilling (s.)	1 crown (cr.)	= 5s.
20 shillings (s.)	= 1 pound (£)	1 guinea (gn.)	= £1 1s.
1 florin	= 2 shillings		

The metric system tables are given in the chapter on decimals and the metric system (Chapter 7).

SPECIAL UNITS

12 units = 1 dozen (doz.)	144 units = 1 gross
20 units = 1 score	

CHAPTER ONE

THE BIRTH OF ARITHMETIC

1. The Origins of Arithmetic

In early days counting was unknown and unnecessary. Animals were killed for food and their skins were used for clothing. A skin could be exchanged for an axe, and such a simple system of barter was adequate for the needs of primitive races. A shepherd tending his flock thousands of years ago could not have told us how many sheep he had. He could not have counted beyond two, but he would have known if one sheep were missing, for he thought of them as individuals not as numbers.

Our modern arithmetic has arisen largely because we no longer barter goods. It would not be practical in our complex way of life. We have to buy and sell, so a system of coinage has become necessary, and with it has developed a technique of calculation. People have come to live in communities, villages and towns. To provide for their needs it has proved necessary to estimate populations, and quantities of food and materials needed by them.

The development of arithmetic has been erratic, sometimes advancing by bounds and sometimes making little progress for several centuries because of difficulties in counting systems. For example the Roman numerals were quite easily added, but were troublesome to manipulate in other ways.

2. Development of Numerals

Long ago people learned to count up to five, largely because there are five fingers on one hand. This gave rise to the seximal scale (or scale of six) in which numbers read 0, 1, 2, 3, 4, 5, 10, 11, 12 .... This system is still the basis of counting in some parts of the world and the illustration of the Oriental abacus (or counting frame) below, which is in the author's possession, is clearly designed for use in this system. Such abacuses are still in use in China and Japan, where they are called *suan pan* and *soroban* respectively. The abacus is also reputed to be still in widespread use in Russia. Great skill can be developed in the use of counting-frames, and ordinary calculations can be carried out as quickly by this method as by our system with pen and paper.

One of the stumbling blocks to the progress of arithmetic was the concept of zero. Men were able to under-

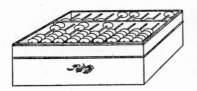
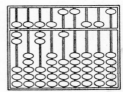

stand the symbol 3, say, representing 3 horses, 3 cabbages or 3 loaves. It required more subtle thought to appreciate that a man who did not have a horse was the same as a man who owned 0 horses. Oddly enough, the author was enlightened to read in one of our national daily newspapers which specialises in letters from readers, in reply to a mother who asked whether 12 times 0 was equal to 0, as given in her son's exercise book, was correct, words approximating to "Don't be a fool, woman. Nought times any number doesn't change it. Nought times twelve is twelve." The author bowed his head. He had always understood that when a gift of nothing was made twelve times the recipient did not materially benefit.

Once zero was understood great strides were made in the development of arithmetic. The decimal scale, originating in the use of all ten fingers, soon predominated, but other scales also had their day. The Babylonians counted in a scale of 60. The sexagesimal scale has survived in our measure of angle and of time. $60'' = 1'$, $60' = 1°$ and $360° = 1$ complete rotation (angle); 60 seconds = 1 minute, 60 minutes = 1 hour (time). Some tropical races used a scale of 20, because they walked barefoot and used fingers and toes in counting.

A few examples of ancient and modern numerals are shown below:

Readers who have played the game of "Mah-Jongg" will have seen the Chinese numerals on the set of pieces (or cards) called Characters.

3. Money, Weights and Measures

The ancient system of barter broke down as civilisation developed. Suppose, for example, a cobbler makes a new pair of shoes for a carpenter. The carpenter offers to make some furniture for the cobbler's home, but the cobbler already has as much as he needs. The carpenter has to find someone who will take a table in exchange for something the cobbler needs. He is lucky. The butcher needs a table. He gives meat in exchange. The cobbler says he has plenty of meat. The tailor, however, needs it and presents the carpenter with a coat in exchange. This the cobbler accepts and the transaction is completed.

Now this is all very well, but the carpenter would have been put to considerable trouble to arrange this cycle of events. What could be done?

The invention of tokens, small and easily carried and accepted by all as representative of potential purchasing power was clearly the answer, so we find the origins of

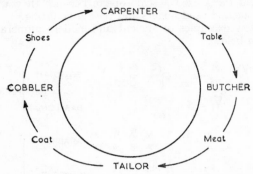

currency. It has taken many strange forms. Red Indians used "wampum", strings of beads in carefully measured lengths. In Cochin China, a strange "coinage" existed.[1]

$$
\left\{
\begin{array}{l}
40 \text{ hoes} = 1 \text{ earthenware jar} \\
7 \text{ jars} = 1 \text{ buffalo} \\
6 \text{ buffaloes} = 1 \text{ slave}
\end{array}
\right.
$$

Each part of the world has naturally developed its own system of weights and measures, but nowadays with so much international trade existing, it might reasonably be expected that there would be some uniformity of coinage.

This unfortunately is far from realisation. It is only necessary to consider for a moment the rates of exchange given below on 23rd May, 1957.

Place		
New York	$2.79	
Montreal	$2.66⅔	Value of £1 at the city
Paris	984¾ fr.	named.
Amsterdam	10.65⅛ fl.	

[1] M. E. Bowman: "Romance in Arithmetic."

Even where the coinage is the same (for example U.S.A. and Canada), the problem is not altogether solved, for exchange depends on the purchasing power of money in the country of origin. In the above table it will be observed that \$2.79 U.S. = £1 = \$2.66⅔ Canada.

There is no necessity however to make matters as complicated as we have in this country. A cursory inspection of the tables of weights and measures on pages xiii to xv will make it clear how complicated mastering of basic processes can be. Can we really uphold a system of dry measure: 2 pints = 1 quart, 4 quarts = 1 gallon, 2 gallons = 1 peck, 4 pecks = 1 bushel, 8 bushels = 1 quarter?

The following example illustrates our elaborate system of linear measure. We have:

12 inches = 1 foot (ft.)	4 poles = 1 chain (ch.)
3 feet = 1 yard (yd.)	10 chains = 1 furlong (fur.)
5½ yards = 1 pole (p.)	8 furlongs = 1 mile (mi.)

Consider[1]

mi.	fur.	ch.	p.	yd.	ft.	in.
3	7	9	3	5	1	7
						2×
2)8	0	0	0	0	0	2
4	**0**	**0**	**0**	**0**	**0**	**1**

We have kept all quantities the right size. We then multiplied a quantity of less than 4 miles by 2. We divided the result by 2 and arrived at a total greater than 4 miles—or so it seems! The fault lies in our curious system of measurement. The student will no doubt discover it for himself, if not at once, then after working Chapter 6.

Compare this with the metric system (Chapter 7). One standard unit exists for weight (gramme) and one for length (metre). Everything else is found by multiplying by powers of ten, e.g. 1 *kilo*gramme = 1000 grammes, 1 *centi*metre = $\frac{1}{100}$ metre.

[1] Second Penguin Problems Book.

Our money, also, is difficult to handle. How much easier than 12d. = 1s., 20s. = £1 is 100 cents = $1 (one dollar)!

We conclude the chapter with one or two examples of calculation from other times and countries.

Ex. 1.

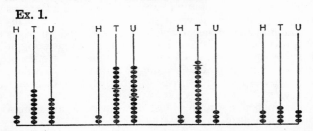

Addition with the ancient abacus. Problem: add 57 and 286. (The headings stand for hundreds (H), tens (T), units (i.e. numbers less than 10) U.)

(1) Put 2 pebbles in H column, 8 in T column, 6 in U column = 286.

(2) Add 5 in T column and 7 in U column = 57 added

(3) Throw out 10 in U column, add 1 in T column.

(4) Throw out 10 in T column, add 1 in H column.

Answer **343** (or more probably CCCXLIII).

Ex. 2. Multiplication used by the peasants of Russia, involving the two times table and division by 2 only.

Multiply 27 by 73.

27	73
13	146
6	292
3	584
1	1168
	——
	1971

The explanation is as follows. Put the smaller number in the first column. Divide by 2 again and again ignoring remainders where present, placing the result underneath each time. Put the larger number in the second column. Double it again and again, placing the result underneath each time.

Strike out all numbers in the second column which come opposite *even* numbers in the first column. Add up the rest.

Ex. 3. We conclude with an example of multiplication in the 15th century. This is particularly interesting in that it is much simpler than our present system but has a drawback. It involves drawing a diagram, called a *grid*, before commencing battle.

Multiply 293 by 347.

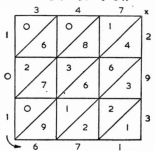

347 times 293 equals **101,671.**

Explanation. (i) Multiply each figure of the top line by each figure down the right-hand side, filling in the results as shown.

(ii) Read off the totals diagonally downwards, starting by taking the units (1) in the bottom right-hand corner, tens $4 + 6 + 6 + 1 + 9 = 26$, put down 6, carry 2 to next diagonal, and so on.

Advantages. This method never requires multiplication by more than 9. All figures are put down at once, and all multiplication is completed before addition takes place.

Disadvantages. A careful diagram is necessary and for large numbers it tends to take up a considerable amount of room. Also the diagram changes shape from number to number (e.g. 3602×27 is 4 squares by 2 squares, 293×347 (above) is 3 squares by 3 squares).

Intelligent children of about 9 years of age have been shown this method and have taken some 2 minutes or less to master it! Adults do not require so long.

CHAPTER TWO

ARITHMETIC—THE FOUR RULES

1. What is Arithmetic?

Arithmetic is the study of the numbers 1, 2, 3, 4 . . . under various operations of which the simplest are addition, subtraction, multiplication and division. These are the so-called "Four Rules". Later we shall add other processes and learn to apply them to everyday life.

Speed and accuracy in simple calculations must first be mastered, and the student is advised to work as many examples as possible.

The symbols used nowadays are Arabic in origin, this system being much simpler to use than the previous Roman method. Imagine a multiplication sum, MDCXL multiplied by CCLIX!

The word "Arithmetic" is derived from the Greek *arithmos*, meaning number.

2. Numbers

The numbers we use are said to be in the scale of ten, that is, when a number is multiplied by 10 it is placed in the next space to the left, e.g. | | 5 | 6 | times 10 becomes | 5 | 6 | 0 |.

For example, 4 3 6 5 consists of:

4 thousands 3 hundreds 6 tens and 5 units, i.e.
4000 and 300 and 60 and 5.

If we were to multiply this number by 10 we would have 4 3 6 5 0, in which the 4 stands for 4 ten-thousands, the 3 for 3 thousands, and so on.

Other scales are sometimes used and to these brief reference will be made for interest in the last chapter of this book. The binary scale (or scale of two) is of great importance in the theory of modern electronic computing machines.

3. Tables

It is necessary that the student should be fully conversant with the multiplication tables up to the 12-times table, and an abbreviated form of table is given with the tables of weights and measures for completeness (page xiii).

Celerity in addition and subtraction is also of value, and it is recommended when adding, say, 7, 12, 5 and 8, that instead of saying mentally "7 and 12 are 19, 19 and 5 are 24, 24 and 8 are **32**" the shorter method "7, 19, 24, **32**" be practised.

4. The Four Rules

(a) **Addition.** The symbol for addition is + (plus), from the Latin, meaning more; it is placed between two numbers to be added together. Thus, $8 + 7$ means "eight plus seven" or "seven added to eight". We can use the symbol repeatedly between numbers to be added, e.g. $8 + 4 + 9 + 12$.

The symbol = means "is equal to", so from above we have

(a) $8 + 7 = 15$
(b) $8 + 4 + 9 + 12 = 33$.

We can add either in a *row* or in a *column*, but when the numbers are large we always use the latter method.

Ex. 1. $17 + 5 + 123 = 145$.

The units are first added: $7 + 5 + 3 = 15$; put down **5**, carry 1.

The tens are next added: $1 + 0 + 2 = 3$, add 1 carried from units; put down **4**.

Hundreds column: put down **1**.

Result **145**.

Ex. 2. Add together 73, 1204 and 513.

We have
$$
\begin{array}{r}
73 \\
1204 \\
513 \\
\hline
1790 \\
\scriptstyle 1
\end{array}
$$

Adding the units, $3 + 4 + 3 = 10$; put down **0,** carry 1 to tens column.

Adding the tens, $7 + 0 + 1 = 8$, add 1 carried from units, giving **9.**

Adding the hundreds, $2 + 5 = 7$. Put down **7.**

Thousands; Put down **1.**

Result **1790.**

Great care must be taken in working in columns, to see that units appear under units, tens under tens, and so on. The units column is the guide to the lay-out.

Ex. 3. Jones has to undertake a business trip to Newcastle-upon-Tyne calling at Cambridge, Nottingham, Sheffield and Leeds on the way. He starts at London. How far has he to go?

From the A.A. Road Book:

London–Cambridge	51
Cambridge–Nottingham	84
Nottingham–Sheffield	37
Sheffield–Leeds	33
Leeds–Newcastle	92
	297 miles.
	$\scriptstyle 2\,1$

The carrying figure from the units column is placed under the tens column, and that from the tens column is placed under the hundreds column. It is then placed in the hundreds column as there are no other hundreds to add.

For certain purposes, where accuracy is of prime importance, the following system of checking results can be used.

Ex. 4. In an examination, Smith, Brown, Jones, and Robinson had 5 questions to answer, each carrying 20 marks. The following table gives the results:

Name	Question No.					Max. 100
	1	2	3	4	5	
Smith	16	9	18	20	12	75
Brown	8	14	3	16	15	56
Jones	15	17	5	17	14	68
Robinson	12	14	2	13	14	55
	51	54	28	66	55	**254**

Although the results shown in the last column may give all that is required, by adding the total marks gained in each *question* and then summing the results in the bottom row, and also in the last column, and seeing that the total (254) is the same both ways, we obtain a valuable check on accuracy. It is also interesting to note that this table shows clearly that there was some weakness in answering question 3, where a total of only 28 marks was gained by all candidates out of a possible 80.

Exercise 1

1. Add together 17, 12, 6 and 8.

2. Find the value of $3 + 7 + 19 + 5 + 8$.

3. Add (a) 124   (b) 1496   (c) 4009
             37   302   378
            209   617   9152

4. Six workmen, Williams, Brown, Andrews, Jenkins, Smart and Thompson receive varying wages from a factory according to the amount of overtime done. In four successive weeks, they are paid as follows:

  Williams £ 14, 12, 16, 15
  Brown   £ 12, 15, 17, 12

Andrews	£ 15, 16, 15, 18
Jenkins	£ 14, 11, 16, 15
Smart	£ 9, 10, 12, 10
Thompson	£ 17, 20, 16, 21

Find how much each receives, and the total wages bill of the factory for the 4 weeks. Check your working as in Ex. 4 above.

(b) Subtraction. The symbol for subtraction is — (minus), from the Latin, meaning less; it is placed between two numbers, when the second is to be taken away from the first. For example, $12 - 9$ means "twelve minus nine" or "nine taken away from twelve"; $12 - 9 = 3$.

Ex. 5. $147 - 59 = $ **88.**

Here we cannot take 9 from 7, so we borrow from the tens column and read as follows: 17 take 9 gives **8**, put down; add back 1 to the 5 to be taken away, to make up for the 1 borrowed. Read 14 take 6 gives **8**, and put this in the tens column of the answer.

Ex. 6. In a mixed school of 1,847 children, there are 792 girls. How many boys are there?

$$18^147$$
$$7_192$$
$$\overline{\quad\textbf{1055}\quad}$$

By putting 1 borrowed from hundreds column next to the 4, making 14 tens and repaying it by putting it under the 7 in the hundreds column, we proceed as follows.

$$\left.\begin{array}{l} 7 \text{ take } 2 \text{ gives } \textbf{5} \\ 14 \text{ take } 9 \text{ gives } \textbf{5} \\ 8 \text{ take } (7 + 1) \text{ gives } \textbf{0} \\ 1 \text{ take } 0 \text{ gives } \textbf{1} \end{array}\right\} \text{Result } \textbf{1055}$$

We can use $+$ and $-$ signs in the same line, indicating amounts added and subtracted.

Ex. 7. Williams had 54 Savings Certificates. He bought

12 more but later sold 30 of them to pay for a new radio. How many had he left?

$$54 + 12 - 30 = 66 - 30$$
$$= \mathbf{36}$$

(i) We *add* the numbers to be *added* first.

(ii) We *add* the numbers to be *taken away*. (In the above example there was only one such number.)

(iii) We *take* the second result from the *first* result.

Ex. 8. $43 + 8 - 24 - 16 = 51 - 40$
$$= \mathbf{11}$$

Ex. 9. In an election there were 3 candidates, Messrs. White, Brown and Black. Mr. White secured 12,542 votes. Mr. Brown had 8,577 votes. If the total number of votes cast was 31,790 how many people voted for Mr. Black?

In this problem it is better to work as follows because of the large numbers.

12,542 (+)	31,790 (−)
8,577	21,119
21,119	**10,671**

Mr. Black secured 10,671 votes.

Here we have added the total of votes not cast for Mr. Black, and subtracted the result from all the votes cast.

EXERCISE 2

1. Subtract (*a*) 41 from 57   (*b*) 38 from 83.

2. Find the value of (*a*) 271 − 141   (*b*) 328 − 279.

3. A school has 54 boys under 12, 57 under 13 but over 12, 62 under 14 but over 13, 53 under 15 but over 14, and 60 under 16 but over 15. Altogether there are 352 boys in the school. How many are over 16?

4. Fill in the blanks with + or − in the right places.

(*a*) 8   4   17 = 29
(*b*) 25   8   3 = 20
(*c*) 36   15   24 = 27
(*d*) 17   5   = 37   25.

(c) **Multiplication.** When we have a number added to itself several times, we shorten the process considerably by multiplication. If seven rows of strawberry plants are laid out in a garden with 12 plants in each row, we could either add:

$$12 + 12 + 12 + 12 + 12 + 12 + 12 = 84 \quad (7 \text{ lots of } 12)$$

or

$$7 + 7 + 7 + 7 + 7 + 7 + 7 + 7 + 7 + 7 + 7 + 7 = 84$$
$$(12 \text{ lots of } 7).$$

The working is greatly reduced by writing either $7 \times 12 = 84$ or $12 \times 7 = 84$, and reading as "seven times twelve equals eighty-four" or "twelve times seven equals eighty-four". The symbol $\times$ means "multiplied by" or "times".

A set of multiplication tables is given on page xiii as mentioned earlier, and these should be memorised.

Ex. 10. What is the cost of a fleet of a dozen taxis at £827 each?

$$827 \times 12$$
$$12$$
$$\overline{}$$
$$9924 \qquad \text{Total cost } \textbf{£9924.}$$
$$3\,8$$

The carrying figures can be placed under the correct columns as in addition.

$12 \times 7 = 84$; put down **4**, carry 8.
$12 \times 2 = 24$; add 8, making 32, put down **2**, carry 3.
$12 \times 8 = 96$; add 3, making 99, put down **99**.

For numbers greater than 12, long multiplication is employed. We then multiply by the units, then the tens and so on.

Ex. 11. Multiply 742 by 397.
We can think of it as 742×7 added to 742×90 added to 742×300. Now multiplying by 10 is achieved by adding a nought to the number.

∴ 742 × 90 = 7420 × 9; 742 × 300 = 74200 × 3.

$$742 \times 397$$
$$397$$

	5194	(= 742 × 7)
(i)	6678	(= 7420 × 9)
(ii)	2226	(= 74200 × 3)

294,574

We do not actually write the noughts indicated but move the figures along one place to the left, so that units become tens and so on in line (i) above; we move the figures two places to the left in line (ii) above, so that the units become hundreds.

EXERCISE 3

1. Multiply (a) 17 by 5   (b) 23 by 7   (c) 168 by 9
(d) 214 by 11.

2. Find the value of (a) 34 × 12   (b) 417 × 6   (c) 3925 × 8   (d) 9579 × 12.

3. Evaluate (a) 317 × 16   (b) 624 × 19   (c) 529 × 73
(d) 8912 × 106.

4. Find the value of 23 × 7 × 9 × 4.
[Hint. 23 × 7 × 9 × 4 = 161 × 9 × 4, and so on.]

5. Evaluate 3401 × 17 × 5.

(d) Division. Division is the process of sharing. The sign for division is ÷; for example, 12 ÷ 3 means "twelve divided by three" or "if twelve were divided into three equal groups, how many would there be in each group."

Ex. 12. 132 ÷ 12 = **11** (because 12 lots of 11 make 132).

Ex. 13. Divide 4988 by 4.
We proceed as follows:

$$\overset{\scriptscriptstyle 1\ 2}{4)4988}$$
$$\overline{\quad 1247\quad}$$

The steps are 4 into 4 divides **1**, put down **1**; 4 into 9 divides **2**, put down, and carry 1 to next column; 1 hundred + 8 tens = 18 tens (i.e. we place the 1 in front of the 8); 4 into 18 divides **4**, put down, and carry 2 to next column; 2 tens + 8 units = 28 units; 4 into 28 divides **7**, put down. Result **1247**.

This process is called *short division*.

When the number by which we divide (called the *divisor*) is greater than twelve we usually resort to *long division*, shown below.

Ex. 14. Find the value of 1161 ÷ 43.

$$\begin{array}{r} 27 \\ 43)\overline{1161} \\ 86 \\ \hline 301 \\ 301 \\ \hline \dots \end{array}$$

Result **27**.

The number by which we divide (43 in this case) is the *divisor*.

The number into which we divide (1161) is the *dividend*.
The number obtained (27) is the *quotient*.

The process is as follows: 43 will not divide into 1 or 11 but it will go into 116. We try the largest number of times it will go, i.e. **2**. Put this in the quotient space and write the result of 43 × 2, i.e. 86, under the 116 and subtract. We get 3 (hundreds) o (tens). Bring down the 1 (unit), giving 301. 43 goes into 301 *seven* times exactly. Enter **7** in the quotient next to the **2**, obtaining **27**.

It often happens that division cannot be carried out exactly.

Ex. 15. A car travels 31 miles on a gallon of petrol. How many gallons are needed for a journey of 387 miles?

$$
\begin{array}{r}
12 \\
31\overline{)387} \\
31 \\
\overline{} \\
77 \\
62 \\
\overline{} \\
15
\end{array}
$$

15 ← Remainder.

The result is **12, remainder 15,** i.e. $12\frac{15}{31}$.

Here we see that 12 gallons are needed, plus 15 parts out of 31 parts of a gallon (i.e. $\frac{15}{31}$ of a gallon—see fractions later). This is very nearly $12\frac{1}{2}$ gallons.

As garages do not sell petrol in this way, the wise motorist would request 13 gallons on his journey.

Another method of division for many numbers greater than 12 is shown in the chapter on Factors.

A little thought will show that the above examples are based on the principle

Dividend = Divisor × Quotient + Remainder.

(The multiplication sign applies only to the quantity on either side of it, not to the Remainder.)

Ex. 16. What number when divided by 7 gives a quotient of 9 and a remainder 4?

$$
\begin{aligned}
\text{Dividend} &= 7 \times 9 + 4 \\
&= 63 + 4 \\
&= \mathbf{67}
\end{aligned}
$$

EXERCISE 4

1. Divide (a) 3177 by 9   (b) 2706 by 11   (c) 298,554 by 37.
2. Express 36,456 pence in shillings.
3. 1102 people attend a lecture and are seated on chairs 29 in a row. How many rows are there?
4. What is the smallest number above 2554 which is exactly divisible by 7?

A. — 2

5. The circumference of a bicycle wheel is 82 inches. How many times will it rotate in travelling 100 yards?

5. Brackets and Miscellaneous Signs

Brackets are used when a group of numbers is to be treated as a single number.

Ex. 17. $\qquad 3 \times (4 + 5) = 3 \times 9$
$$= 27.$$

Ex. 18. $\qquad 42 - (17 + 3) = 42 - 20$
$$= 22.$$

The part inside the bracket is worked out first. More than one pair of brackets may be used, and in this case the innermost bracket is evaluated first.

Ex. 19.
$$6 \times (3 + 4) - 4 \times (5 - 2) = 6 \times 7 - 4 \times 3$$
$$= 42 - 12$$
$$= 30.$$

Ex. 20.
$$63 - \{7 + 2 \times (8 - 5)\} = 63 - \{7 + 2 \times 3\}$$
$$= 63 - \{7 + 6\}$$
$$= 63 - 13$$
$$= 50.$$

When using different signs together as above, the word BODMAS is helpful, indicating:

1	B	Brackets
2	O	Of
3	D	Division
4	M	Multiplication
5	A	Addition
6	S	Subtraction

This gives the order in which the working must be done, starting with 1 (Brackets).
"Of" means "multiply", but is not often used, e.g. 5 of 7 = 35.

1. Deal with inside of Brackets.
2. Work out Of (if any).
3. Work out Division.
4. Work out Multiplication.
5 and 6. Work out Addition and Subtraction as previously explained.

Ex. 21. Simplify 3 of $(12 - 7) + 56 \div (9 - 5)$.

The expression	= 3 of $5 + 56 \div 4$	Rule 1
	= $15 + 56 \div 4$	Rule 2
	= $15 + 14$	Rule 3
	= **29.**	Rule 5

EXERCISE 5

1. Add together (a) $24 + 6 + 9 + 17$ (b) $23 + 5 + 67 + 8$ (c) $424 + 137 + 19$.

2. Add
   (a) 21, 43, 162
   (b) 231, 79, 928
   (c) 25, 2077, 165, 4821
   (d) 31,725, 9,406, 784, 23,209

3. Subtract (a) 147 from 308.   (b) 49 from 2116.

4. Find the value of (a) $627 - 239$.   (b) $4006 - 1879$.

5. Add 243, 1629, 17 and 405, and subtract 298 from the result.

6. Find the value of $2971 + 3046 - 2188$.

7. Multiply (a) 217 by 9   (b) 46 by 17   (c) 837 by 29   (d) 251 by 367.

8. Find the value of (a) 1247×8 (b) 304×73 (c) 295×174 (d) 3528×208.

9. Find the value of (a) $108 \div 9$ (b) $259 \div 7$ (c) $1465 \div 5$ (d) $25073 \div 6$.

10. Divide (a) 2148 by 43   (b) 2242 by 59   (c) 3207 by 88   (d) 20173 by 133.

11. Simplify (a) $61 + (23 - 15) \times 2$
   (b) $30 - (17 + 4) \div 3$
   (c) $4 + 2 \times \{3 + 4 \times (8 - 3) - 6\}$
   (d) 3 of $(5 + 2) - 2 \times (3 + 7) \div 5$.

12. Simplify (a) $6 - 12 \div 4 + 3 \times 8$
            (b) $73 - \{65 \times 2 - (14 \times 5 - 8)\}$.

13. A book has 195 pages. There are about 284 words on each page. How many words are there in the book?

14. Queen Elizabeth I came to the throne in 1558 and died in 1603. How long did she reign?

15. A train consists of an engine of weight 95 tons; a tender of weight 40 tons and 12 carriages each weighing 32 tons. What is the total weight of the train?

16. 10,000 cabbages are planted, 85 in a row. How many rows are there? (The last row is incomplete.)

17. How many screws are there in 16 boxes each containing a gross?

18. George Orwell has written a book called "1984". How many hours will there be in that year?

19. Smith earns £13 a week. How much does he get in a year?

20. A train starts on a journey of 760 miles across Europe. After travelling for 17 hours at an average speed of 41 miles per hour, how much farther has it to go?

21. How many seconds are there in a day?

22. In working out the multiplication sum 1723 × 27 a boy misreads the first number as 1732. What is the error in his answer?

23. How many numbers between 100 and 1000 are:

       (a) not divisible by 2
       (b) not divisible by 3
       (c) not divisible by either 2 or 3?

24. A motorist pays £28 a year for tax and insurance on his car. Repairs cost him £30 a year. He averages 150 miles travel a week in the car, and uses one gallon of petrol every 30 miles, and one pint of oil every 300 miles. If petrol costs 6s. a gallon and oil is 2s. a pint, how much a year does it cost him to run the car?

CHAPTER THREE

FACTORS

1. Factors

Consider $12 = 3 \times 4$. 3 and 4 are said to be *factors* of 12. 12 is also equal to 6×2 and to 1×12, so all the numbers 1, 2, 3, 4, 6, 12 are factors of 12. 12 is said to be a *multiple* of 3, and of 6, and in fact of any of these numbers. We are thus led to the definition of factor.

A number x is a factor of another number y, if x divides exactly into y (or if y is a multiple of x).

Many numbers have no factors other than themselves and *unity* (i.e. one), e.g. $7 = 1 \times 7$, but 7 has no other factors; 13 possesses only factors 1 and 13. These numbers are called *prime numbers*. The simplest ones are 1, 2, 3, 5, 7, 11, 13, 17, 19, 23, 29. . . .

For generations attempts have been made to obtain a formula to give prime numbers only but they have all failed. The method below, known as the "Sieve of Eratosthenes" will enmesh all numbers up to the largest written down.

Strike out all multiples of 2.
Then all multiples of 3 left
Then all multiples of 5 left
Then all multiples of 7 left (there are none left in this diagram) and so on.

1	2	3	4	5	6	7	8
9	10	11	12	13	14	15	16
17	18	19	20	21	22	23	24
25	26	27	28	29	30	31	32
33	34	35	36	37	38	39	40

etc.

The numbers 2, 3, 5, 7 are not themselves deleted. The numbers remaining are the prime numbers.

2. Tests for Factors

The following tests are very useful and are worth memorising:

(1) A number is divisible by **2,** if the last figure is even (e.g. 1658).

(2) A number is divisible by **3,** if the sum of the figures is divisible by 3 (e.g. 4251 is divisible by 3, because $4 + 2 + 5 + 1 = 12$, which is divisible by 3).

(3) A number is divisible by **4,** if the number formed by the last 2 figures is divisible by 4 (e.g. 30528 is divisible by 4, because 28 is divisible by 4).

(4) A number is divisible by **5,** if it ends in 0 or 5 (e.g. 20730 and 1945 are both divisible by 5).

(5) A number is divisible by **6** if it satisfies (1) and (2) above (e.g. 21354 is divisible by 2 and by 3, therefore by $2 \times 3 = 6$).

(6) A number is divisible by **8** if the last three figures are divisible by 8 (e.g. 217584 is divisible by 8, because 584 is divisible by 8).

(7) A number is divisible by **9,** if the sum of the figures is divisible by 9 (e.g. 8352 is divisible by 9, because $8 + 3 + 5 + 2 = 18$ is divisible by 9).

(8) A number is divisible by 10, 100, 1000, . . . if it ends in 0, 00, 000 . . . (e.g. 7920 is divisible by 10, 304000 is divisible by 1000).

Tests (1), (3) and (6) above are similar in nature.

Tests (2) and (7) are related; also test (4) can be associated with test (8).

Tests exist for some other factors, but they are more complicated and would be out of place here.[1]

3. Prime Factors

We have seen that $12 = 4 \times 3$. Now 3 is a prime number but 4 is not, but $4 = 2 \times 2$, and 2 is prime.

∴ **$12 = 2 \times 2 \times 3$,** and the number 12 is said to be expressed in its prime factors. They are written in ascending order of magnitude.

---

[1] One such test is based on the fact that $7 \times 11 \times 13 = 1001$.

Ex. 1. Express 2565 in prime factors.

$$2565 = 5 \times 513 = 5 \times 9 \times 57$$
$$= 5 \times 9 \times 3 \times 19 \text{ (using the tests above)}$$
$$= \mathbf{3 \times 3 \times 3 \times 5 \times 19.}$$

4. Indices

The writing of prime factors is considerably reduced if indices are used.

In $2 \times 2 \times 2 = 2^3$, 3 is the *index*. It means that 2 is written down three times and the results are multiplied together. For example $4^5 = 4 \times 4 \times 4 \times 4 \times 4$; $5^4 = 5 \times 5 \times 5 \times 5$. Notice that these are not the same number.

Ex. 2. $2565 = 3 \times 3 \times 3 \times 5 \times 19$ from Ex. 1 above
$$= \mathbf{3^3 \times 5 \times 19.}$$

Ex. 3. $7920 = 9 \times 880$
$$= 9 \times 11 \times 80 = 9 \times 11 \times 8 \times 10$$
$$= 2 \times 2 \times 2 \times 2 \times 3 \times 3 \times 5 \times 11$$
$$= \mathbf{2^4 \times 3^2 \times 5 \times 11.}$$

It is usual to give the answer with factors arranged in ascending order of magnitude.

5. Division by Factors

In Chapter One we made reference to a method which can be used quite often for division by a number greater than 12. This applies when the divisor can be put into factors which are less than or equal to 12. We do not necessarily resolve into prime factors in this case, as this may lead to unnecessary working.

Examples of such divisors are $18 = 9 \times 2$, $49 = 7 \times 7$, $154 = 2 \times 7 \times 11$.

Ex. 4. Find the value of $1449 \div 63$.

$63 = 7 \times 9$ 7)1449   Result **23.**
                    9) 207
                      23

We divide by one factor, say 7 as above. Divide the quotient 207 by the other factor 9.

Ex. 5. Divide 1415 by 63.

$$63 = 7 \times 9 \text{ as before} \quad 7 \overline{)1415}$$
$$9\overline{)\ 202} \text{ remainder } 1$$
$$\overline{22} \text{ remainder } 4$$

∴ 1415 ÷ 63 = **22, remainder 29** (or $22\frac{29}{63}$). The remainder is not obvious.

The second remainder 4 was found *after* dividing by 7.

∴ The total remainder was $4 \times 7 + 1 = 29$, on adding in the first remainder.

The method of division by factors is often used in monetary calculations, as will appear later.

EXERCISE I

1. Using the tests for factors find which of the numbers 2, 3, 4, 5, 6 are factors of:

      (*a*) 418   (*b*) 318   (*c*) 5010   (*d*) 30060   (*e*) 11945.

2. Using the tests for factors find which of the following numbers are divisible by *both* 8 and 9:

      (*a*) 3672   (*b*) 20592   (*c*) 7956.

3. Resolve into prime factors without indices:

      (*a*) 18   (*b*) 60   (*c*) 924   (*d*) 3003.

4. Resolve into prime factors using indices:

      (*a*) 48   (*b*) 441   (*c*) 5808   (*d*) 21560.

5. Find, using division by factors, the value of:

      (*a*) 1505 ÷ 35   (*b*) 6816 ÷ 96
      (*c*) 2709 ÷ 77   (*d*) 9148 ÷ 27.

6. Highest Common Factor (H.C.F.)

A *common factor* of two (or more) numbers is a factor which occurs in both of them (or all of them).

The *highest common factor* of a group of numbers is the largest number which will divide into all of them. The H.C.F. of 6 and 9 is 3, because $6 = 2 \times 3$, and $9 = 3 \times 3$, and each contains a 3.

Consider $\left\{\begin{array}{l} 60 = 2 \times 2 \times 3 \times 5 \\ 225 = \phantom{2 \times 2 \times{}} 3 \times 3 \times 5 \times 5 \\ 210 = 2 \times \phantom{2 \times{}} 3 \times 5 \times 7 \end{array}\right.$

All these numbers have common factors 3 and 5 but no others.

Therefore their H.C.F. is $3 \times 5 =$ **15.**

Ex. 6. Find the H.C.F. of 90 and 126.

$$90 = 2 \times 3 \times 3 \times 5$$
$$126 = 2 \times 3 \times 3 \times 7$$

$\therefore$ H.C.F. $= 2 \times 3 \times 3 =$ **18.** (The common factor 3 occurs twice.)

7. Lowest Common Multiple (L.C.M.)

The L.C.M. of two or more numbers is the smallest number into which they will divide exactly. To put it another way, the L.C.M. of a set of numbers is the smallest number which contains each member of the set as a factor.

Finding the L.C.M. of a set of numbers is very important when simplifying *fractions*. (See Chapter 4).

Consider $42 = 2 \times 3 \times 7 = 2 \times 3 \times 7$
$24 = 2 \times 2 \times 2 \times 3 = 2^3 \times 3$
$28 = 2 \times 2 \times 7 = 2^2 \times 7$

$2, 2^2, 2^3$ will all divide into 2^3 but will not *all* divide into any smaller number exactly; also 3 and 7 will divide into 3×7, so the L.C.M. of this set of numbers 24, 28, 42 is $2^3 \times 3 \times 7 =$ **168.**

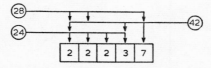

The diagram illustrates the necessity for all the factors $2 \times 2 \times 2 \times 3 \times 7$.

EXERCISE 2

1. Find the H.C.F. of the following sets of numbers:
      (*a*) 42 and 63   (*b*) 48, 64 and 88
      (*c*) 132, 154 and 242   (*d*) 72, 108 and 792.

2. Find the L.C.M. of the following:
      (*a*) 8, 12   (*b*) 3, 4, 8   (*c*) 12, 27, 36
      (*d*) 55, 88, 121   (*e*) 4, 5, 6, 10 (*f*) 84, 63, 42, 36
                     (*g*) 35, 56, 80.

3. Find the smallest number into which 30, 40 and 66 divide exactly.

4. What is the smallest sum of money which can be counted out into exact multiples of 5s., 6s. and 8s.?

5. Square tiles are to be used to cover a wall 25 ft. long to a height of 3 ft. 9 in. exactly. What is the largest possible size of tile? Find how many tiles are needed. (See Chapter 11 on areas.)

6. Three bells are rung at intervals of 6, 8 and 9 seconds respectively. If they start together, how long is it before they are again ringing together?

7. A set of counters is required for a game in which any number of players up to ten may take part. What is the smallest number of counters required, if all the counters must be used on each occasion?

8. How many numbers between 1 and 1000 contain all the numbers 2, 3, 4, 5, 6 as factors?

CHAPTER FOUR

FRACTIONS

1. The Idea of a Fraction

So far the work in this book has been confined to whole numbers, or *integers*, as they are called. We now consider how to deal with parts of whole quantities, called *fractions*.

The most familiar fractions in everyday use are the halfpenny and the farthing. They are written $\frac{1}{2}$d. and $\frac{1}{4}$d. respectively, indicating that they are one-half ($\frac{1}{2}$) and one-quarter ($\frac{1}{4}$) of a penny. The top, called the *numerator*, tells us how many parts we are taking. The bottom, called the *denominator*, tells us how many parts would make a whole one.

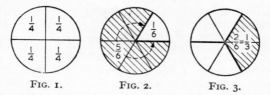

FIG. 1.   FIG. 2.   FIG. 3.

In fig. 1 we see that $\frac{1}{4} + \frac{1}{4} + \frac{1}{4} + \frac{1}{4} = \frac{4}{4}$ (4 quarters) $= 1$ (whole).

Quantities like $\frac{1}{4}$, $\frac{2}{5}$, $\frac{7}{12}$ are called *vulgar* (or *common*) fractions. The quantity $\frac{2}{5}$ means we are taking 2 parts out of 5 parts of a quantity. Consider fig. 2. Suppose it is a cake divided into six equal parts as shown. Each part is $\frac{1}{6}$ of the whole cake. The shaded area is $\frac{5}{6}$ of the whole.

Also

$$\frac{1}{6} + \frac{5}{6} = \frac{1+5}{6} = \frac{6}{6} = 1 \text{ (whole cake, in this case).}$$

27

What happens if the numerator and denominator have a common factor?

In fig. 3 we have divided our cake again into 6 parts but have now taken 2 of them (shaded). Suppose, however, we had divided our cake into 3 parts as indicated by the heavier lines in fig. 3, we would have had the same shaded area as $\frac{1}{3}$ of our cake. ∴ $\frac{2}{6} = \frac{1}{3}$. This leads us to conjecture that we can cancel out common factors in numerator and denominator, e.g.

$$\frac{24}{28} = \frac{\overset{6}{\cancel{24}}}{\underset{7}{\cancel{28}}} = \frac{6}{7} \text{ (on dividing out top and bottom by 4).}$$

The fraction is then said to be "in its lowest terms". We can reverse the idea and say, for example, that $\frac{1}{3} = \frac{2}{6} = \frac{3}{9} = \dots$

2. Definition of a Fraction

A fraction is defined as the quotient (i.e. the ratio) of two quantities.

$$\text{Fraction} = \frac{\text{Numerator}}{\text{Denominator}}.$$

A fraction like $\frac{6}{7}$ (written in words "six-sevenths") in which the numerator is smaller than the denominator is called a *proper fraction*. One like $\frac{17}{12}$, in which the numerator is greater than the denominator, is called an *improper fraction*. The latter can always be reduced to a whole number and a proper fraction, known as a *mixed number*.

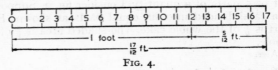

FIG. 4.

Consider fig. 4 which illustrates part of a 2-ft. rule, measured in inches. The length shown is 17 in., i.e. $\frac{17}{12}$ ft.

but it can be thought of as 12 in. plus 5 in., i.e. 1 ft. + $\frac{5}{12}$ ft.

$$\therefore \ \tfrac{17}{12} = 1 + \tfrac{5}{12} = 1\tfrac{5}{12}.$$

We do not, in practice, write down all these steps. For example, $\frac{23}{5} = 4\frac{3}{5}$, is written down at once, for $23 \div 5 = 4 +$ remainder 3 (that is four and three-fifths).

3. Fractions of Standard Quantities

In section 1 above we saw that we could multiply the top and bottom of a fraction by the same number without altering the result; for example

$$\tfrac{2}{3} = \tfrac{2}{3} \times \tfrac{7}{7} = \tfrac{14}{21}.$$

The reason is that $\frac{7}{7} = 1$, so we have multiplied only by 1. We extend the idea below, and the method is important. It will be used, for example, when working long multiplication by practice.

Ex. 1. Find the value of $\frac{1}{5}$ of £1.

$$\tfrac{1}{5} \times £1 = \tfrac{1}{5} \times 20\text{s.} = \textbf{4s.} \quad \left(\frac{1}{5} \times \overset{4}{20} = \frac{20}{5} = 4 \right).$$

Ex. 2. Find the value of $\frac{2}{3}$ of £1.

$$\tfrac{2}{3} \times £1 = \tfrac{2}{3} \times 20\text{s.} = \tfrac{40}{3}\text{s.} = 13\tfrac{1}{3}\text{s.}$$
Now $\tfrac{1}{3}\text{s.} = \tfrac{1}{3} \times 12\text{d.} = 4\text{d.}$
$$\therefore \ \tfrac{2}{3} \text{ of } £1 = \textbf{13s. 4d.}$$

Ex. 3. Calculate $\frac{4}{9}$ of 1 yd.

$$\frac{4}{9} \times 1 \text{ yd.} = \frac{4}{9} \times \overset{4}{36} \text{ in.} = \textbf{16 in.}$$

The reverse process should also be known.

Ex. 4. What fraction is 6s. of £1?

$$\frac{6\text{s.}}{£1} = \frac{6\text{s.}}{20\text{s.}} = \frac{6}{20} = \frac{\textbf{3}}{\textbf{10}}.$$

Ex. 5. What fraction is 6 lb. of 1 stone?

$$\frac{6 \text{ lb.}}{1 \text{ stone}} = \frac{6 \text{ lb.}}{14 \text{ lb.}} = \frac{6}{14} = \frac{3}{7}.$$

It will be noticed in examples 4 and 5 that the fraction may not be worked out until *the same units are used top and bottom*.

EXERCISE 1[1]

Find the value of:

1. $\frac{2}{3}$rds of 1 day.
2. Four-fifths of 1 hr.
3. $\frac{3}{8} \times$ 1 gall.
4. $\frac{7}{10}$ of 2 min.
5. $\frac{4}{5}$ of 8 min.
6. $\frac{7}{16} \times £1$.

Find what fraction:

7. 5d. is of 2s.
8. 4 hr. is of 1 day.
9. 12s. 6d. is of £1 (express top and bottom in sixpences)
10. 21 in. is of 1 yd.
11. 100 sq. in. is of 1 sq. ft.

4. Addition and Subtraction of Fractions

When two fractions have the same *denominator*, addition or subtraction is simple. For example $\frac{1}{5} + \frac{2}{5} = \frac{3}{5}$.

What happens, however, when we wish to handle fractions with different denominators? Suppose we wish to find $\frac{2}{3} - \frac{1}{4}$. We find the L.C.M. of the denominator (see Chapter Two), in this case 12, and express the fractions in terms of denominator 12.

$$\frac{2}{3} = \frac{8}{12}; \frac{1}{4} = \frac{3}{12}$$

$$\therefore \frac{2}{3} - \frac{1}{4} = \frac{8}{12} - \frac{3}{12} = \frac{8-3}{12} = \frac{5}{12}.$$

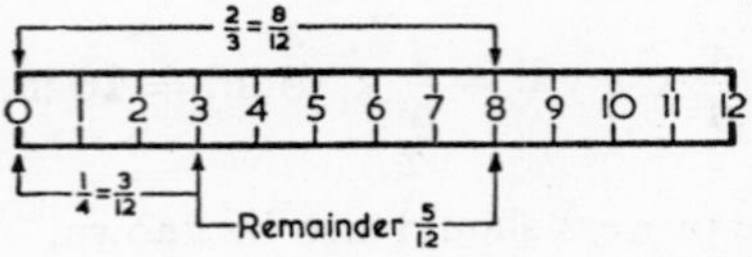

FIG. 5.

The illustration makes the process clear.

[1] The quantities used here all appear in the tables of money, weights and measures, on pages xiii to xv.

Ex. 6. Simplify $\frac{2}{5} + \frac{1}{2} - \frac{5}{6}$.

L.C.M. of denominator $= 30$

$$\therefore \frac{2}{5} + \frac{1}{2} - \frac{5}{6} = \frac{12 + 15 - 25}{30} = \frac{27 - 25}{30}$$

$$= \frac{2}{30} = \frac{1}{15}.$$

$\left(\text{The explanation is as follows:}\right.$

$$\frac{1}{5} = \frac{6}{30} \quad \therefore \frac{2}{5} = \frac{2 \times 6}{30} = \frac{12}{30}.$$

$$\frac{1}{2} = \frac{15}{30}$$

$$\frac{1}{6} = \frac{5}{30} \quad \therefore \frac{5}{6} = \frac{5 \times 5}{30} = \frac{25}{30};$$

$\text{or simply } \dfrac{2}{5} + \dfrac{1}{2} - \dfrac{5}{6} = \dfrac{2 \times 6 + 15 - 5 \times 5}{30}\Big).$

The student should endeavour to work this part of the question mentally as soon as possible, but for the first few examples it is easier and safer to put in the extra step indicated at the end of the bracket.

Ex. 7. Simplify $4\frac{2}{3} - 1\frac{1}{4}$.

$$4\frac{2}{3} - 1\frac{1}{4} = (4 - 1) + \left(\frac{2}{3} - \frac{1}{4}\right)$$

$$= 3 + \frac{8 - 3}{12} = 3\frac{5}{12}.$$

Note that in *addition* and *subtraction* we deal with whole numbers separately.

Ex. 8. Simplify $3\frac{1}{2} - 1\frac{3}{5}$.

$$3\frac{1}{2} - 1\frac{3}{5} = (3 - 1) + \left(\frac{1}{2} - \frac{3}{5}\right)$$

$$= 2 + \frac{5 - 6}{10}$$

$$= 1 + \frac{10 + 5 - 6}{10}$$

$$= 1\frac{9}{10}.$$

(To make the fractional part positive we borrow 1, i.e. $\frac{10}{10}$, from the whole number.)

Ex. 9. Simplify $4\frac{1}{6} - 2\frac{4}{5} + \frac{4}{3}$.

$$4\frac{1}{6} - 2\frac{4}{5} + \frac{4}{3} = 4\frac{1}{6} - 2\frac{4}{5} + 1\frac{1}{3}$$

$$= (4 - 2 + 1) + \left(\tfrac{1}{6} - \tfrac{4}{5} + \tfrac{1}{3}\right)$$

$$= 3 + \left(\tfrac{1}{6} - \tfrac{4}{5} + \tfrac{1}{3}\right)$$

$$= 3 + \frac{5 - 24 + 10}{30} = 3 + \frac{15 - 24}{30}$$

$$= 2 + \frac{30 + 15 - 24}{30} = 2\tfrac{21}{30} = 2\tfrac{7}{10}.$$

Ex. 10. Mary was offered the option of $\frac{7}{9}$ or $\frac{17}{20}$ of a prize of 15s. Which is better?

This kind of problem leads to placing fractions in order of magnitude.

L.C.M. of 9 and 20 is 180.

$$\tfrac{7}{9} = \tfrac{140}{180}, \ \tfrac{17}{20} = \tfrac{153}{180}$$

$\therefore$ **$\frac{17}{20}$ is the bigger amount and is the one Mary should choose.**

EXERCISE 2

Simplify:

1. $\frac{3}{4} + \frac{1}{2}$ **2.** $\frac{2}{3} - \frac{1}{2}$ **3.** $3\frac{1}{2} + \frac{3}{5}$ **4.** $2\frac{1}{2} - 1\frac{3}{8}$

5. $2\frac{1}{4} - \frac{1}{2}$ **6.** $3\frac{1}{3} + 2\frac{3}{4}$ **7.** $4\frac{3}{5} - 2\frac{3}{4}$ **8.** $\frac{51}{14} - \frac{29}{21}$

9. $2\frac{1}{3} + 1\frac{2}{5} - 3\frac{1}{4}$ **10.** $\frac{3}{10} - \frac{7}{20} + 1\frac{1}{100}$

11. $1 + \frac{1}{2} + \frac{1}{4} + \frac{1}{8} + \frac{1}{16} + \frac{1}{32}$ **12.** $7\frac{1}{3} - 3\frac{5}{12} - 2\frac{3}{4}$

5. Multiplication of Fractions

When two or more fractions are multiplied together, we may cancel out factors which appear one in the numerator and one in the denominator.

For example $\dfrac{2}{3} \times \dfrac{3}{4} = \dfrac{\overset{1}{2}}{\underset{1}{3}} \times \dfrac{\overset{1}{3}}{\underset{2}{4}} = \dfrac{1}{2}.$

because the 3's are common, and 2 is also a common factor.

To understand this properly it is necessary to consider the process in two stages:

(i) $\frac{1}{3} \times \frac{3}{4} = \frac{1}{3}$ of $\frac{3}{4} = \frac{3}{12} = \frac{1}{4}$;

(ii) $\frac{2}{3} \times \frac{3}{4} = 2$ of $(\frac{1}{3} \times \frac{3}{4}) = 2 \times \frac{1}{4}$
(from (i))
$= \frac{1}{4} + \frac{1}{4} = \frac{2}{4} = \frac{1}{2}$.

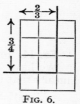

Fig. 6 shows 12 squares, laid out 3 by 4. If we take $\frac{2}{3}$ of the columns $\times \frac{3}{4}$ of the rows we get 6 squares, i.e. $\frac{1}{2}$ of the area.

Fig. 6.

When numerators and denominators do not cancel, we may simplify as follows:

$$\frac{2}{7} \times \frac{3}{5} = \frac{2 \times 3}{7 \times 5} = \frac{6}{35}.$$

We may also use both ideas, as in the quantity

$$\frac{7}{9} \times \frac{3}{4} = \frac{7}{\underset{3}{9}} \times \frac{\overset{1}{3}}{4} = \frac{7}{3 \times 4} = \frac{7}{12}.$$

Ex. 11. Simplify $\frac{7}{10} \times \frac{5}{21}$.

$$\frac{7}{10} \times \frac{5}{21} = \frac{\overset{1}{7} \times \overset{1}{5}}{\underset{2}{10} \times \underset{3}{21}} = \frac{1}{6}.$$

When whole number parts appear in *multiplication* of fractions (i.e. *mixed numbers* occur) the *mixed numbers* must first be converted to *improper fractions* before simplification can take place. This also applies to *division*.

Ex. 12. Simplify $2\frac{1}{4} \times 5\frac{1}{3}$.

$$2\frac{1}{4} \times 5\frac{1}{3} = \frac{\overset{3}{9}}{\underset{1}{4}} \times \frac{\overset{4}{16}}{\underset{1}{3}} = \frac{12}{1} = 12.$$

$(2\frac{1}{4} = \frac{8}{4} + \frac{1}{4} = \frac{9}{4}; \; 5\frac{1}{3} = \frac{15}{3} + \frac{1}{3} = \frac{16}{3})$

Ex. 13. Simplify $1\frac{1}{2} \times 2\frac{2}{3} \times \frac{7}{16}$

$$1\frac{1}{2} \times 2\frac{2}{3} \times \frac{7}{16} = \frac{3}{\underset{1}{2}} \times \frac{\overset{1}{8}}{\underset{1}{3}} \times \frac{7}{\underset{2}{16}} = \frac{7}{4} = 1\frac{3}{4}.$$

Ex. 14. Find the value of $(\frac{2}{3})^3 \times 18s.$

We have already seen that the index 3 to a number means that it occurs 3 times.

$$\therefore (\tfrac{2}{3})^3 \times 18s. = \tfrac{2}{3} \times \tfrac{2}{3} \times \tfrac{2}{3} \times 18s.$$

$$= \frac{2 \times 2 \times 2 \times \overset{\overset{2}{6}}{18} \times \overset{4}{12}}{\underset{1}{3} \times \underset{1}{3} \times \underset{1}{3}} d.$$

$$= 64d. = \textbf{5s. 4d.}$$

6. Division of Fractions

Consider $\frac{3}{7} \div \frac{2}{5}$. It is not obvious what this means. We could, however, write the quantity as follows:

$$\frac{3}{7} \div \frac{2}{5} = \frac{\frac{3}{7} \leftarrow \text{ numerator}}{\frac{2}{5} \leftarrow \text{ denominator}}$$

Now if we multiply top and bottom by the same amount we do not change the quantity.

$$\therefore \frac{\frac{3}{7}}{\frac{2}{5}} = \frac{\frac{3}{7} \times 5 \times 7}{\frac{2}{5} \times 5 \times 7} = \frac{3 \times 5}{2 \times 7} = \frac{3 \times 5}{7 \times 2} = \frac{3}{7} \times \frac{5}{2}$$

We know how to work out the final result (from paragraph 5 above), but the interest lies in the facts that we have *inverted the second expression and multiplied by it* in our steps of reasoning. This leads to the following rule.

When dividing by a fraction, invert it and multiply by the result,

e.g. $\frac{2}{5} \div \frac{9}{11} = \frac{2}{5} \times \frac{11}{9}$; $\frac{4}{7} \div 3 = \frac{4}{7} \times \frac{1}{3}$; $\frac{6}{17} \div \frac{1}{4} = \frac{6}{17} \times 4.$

Note that dividing by 3 is the same as multiplying by $\frac{1}{3}$, for the *reciprocal* (i.e. inverted form of $\frac{3}{1}$ is $\frac{1}{3}$). Similarly the reciprocal of $\frac{1}{4}$ is $\frac{4}{1}$, i.e. 4.

Ex. 15. Simplify $\frac{4}{15} \div \frac{3}{5}$.

$$\frac{4}{15} \div \frac{3}{5} = \frac{4}{\underset{3}{15}} \times \frac{\overset{1}{5}}{3} = \frac{4}{9}.$$

Ex. 16. Simplify $2\frac{1}{7} \div 1\frac{1}{4}$.

$$2\frac{1}{7} \div 1\frac{1}{4} = \frac{15}{7} \div \frac{5}{4} = \frac{\overset{3}{15}}{7} \times \frac{4}{\underset{1}{5}} = \frac{12}{7} = 1\frac{5}{7}.$$

Ex. 17. Find the value of $2\frac{1}{2} \times 3\frac{2}{3} \div 1\frac{4}{7}$.

$$2\frac{1}{2} \times 3\frac{2}{3} \div 1\frac{4}{7} = \frac{5}{2} \times \frac{11}{3} \div \frac{11}{7} = \frac{5}{2} \times \frac{\overset{1}{11}}{3} \times \frac{7}{\underset{1}{11}}$$

$$= \frac{35}{6} = 5\frac{5}{6}.$$

EXERCISE 3

Simplify:

1. $\frac{4}{7} \times \frac{2}{3}$ **2.** $\frac{3}{8} \times 1\frac{2}{3}$ **3.** $1\frac{2}{5} \times 2\frac{3}{7}$ **4.** $\left(\frac{3}{4}\right)^2$

5. $2\frac{1}{5} \times 3\frac{3}{4} \times 4\frac{1}{3}$ **6.** $\left(\frac{2}{5}\right)^2 \times 12\frac{1}{2}$ **7.** $\left(\frac{2}{3}\right)^3 \times \left(\frac{3}{4}\right)^2$

8. $\frac{3}{4} \div \frac{2}{3}$ **9.** $1 \div \frac{3}{8}$ **10.** $2 \div 1\frac{1}{3}$ **11.** $\frac{3}{4} \div 1\frac{1}{2}$

12. $2\frac{3}{7} \div 2\frac{1}{10}$ **13.** $3 \times \frac{2}{5} \div 3\frac{1}{3}$ **14.** $1\frac{2}{5} \times 3\frac{4}{7} \div 2\frac{1}{2}$.

7. Mixed Signs

In simplifying fractions in which brackets and other signs occur we merely apply the rule BODMAS given in Chapter 1.

Ex. 18. Evaluate $\frac{1}{2} \div \frac{1}{3} - 1\frac{1}{4}$.

$\frac{1}{2} \div \frac{1}{3} - 1\frac{1}{4} = \frac{1}{2} \times 3 - 1\frac{1}{4}$ (*Divide*, before *Subtracting*)

$\qquad = \frac{3}{2} - 1\frac{1}{4} = 1\frac{1}{2} - 1\frac{1}{4}$

$\qquad = \frac{1}{2} - \frac{1}{4} = \frac{2-1}{4} = \frac{1}{4}.$

Care is needed in applying the rules to these mixed cases and, although short cuts are often possible, they are not advised until experience is gained.

Ex. 19. Simplify $2\frac{1}{2} \times 1\frac{1}{3} - \frac{3}{5} \div 1\frac{4}{11}$.

$$2\frac{1}{2} \times 1\frac{1}{3} - \frac{3}{5} \div 1\frac{4}{11} = \frac{5}{2} \times \frac{4}{3} - \frac{3}{5} \div \frac{15}{11} \qquad \text{(Improper Fractions)}$$

$$= \frac{5}{2} \times \frac{\overset{2}{4}}{3} - \frac{3}{5} \times \frac{\overset{1}{11}}{\underset{5}{15}} \qquad \text{(Division)}$$

$$= \frac{10}{\underset{1}{3}} - \frac{11}{\underset{5}{25}} \qquad \text{(Multiplication)}$$

$$= 3\frac{1}{3} - 1\frac{11}{25} = 3 + \frac{25 - 33}{75}$$
$$\text{(Subtraction)}$$

$$= 2 + \frac{75 + 25 - 33}{75} = 2 + \frac{67}{75}$$

$$= 2\frac{67}{75}.$$

Ex. 20. Simplify $1\frac{1}{2} \div (2\frac{4}{9} \times 1\frac{4}{11})$.

Here the bracket has complete priority.

$$2\frac{4}{9} \times 1\frac{4}{11} = \frac{\overset{2}{22}}{9} \times \frac{\overset{5}{15}}{\underset{}{11}} = \frac{10}{3}$$

$$\therefore \ 1\frac{1}{2} \div (2\frac{4}{9} \times 1\frac{4}{11}) = 1\frac{1}{2} \div \frac{10}{3} = \frac{3}{2} \div \frac{10}{3}$$
$$= \frac{3}{2} \times \frac{3}{10} = \frac{9}{20}.$$

Ex. 21. Simplify $\dfrac{3\frac{1}{3} + 1\frac{1}{4} \text{ of } \frac{2}{5}}{2\frac{2}{5} - 1\frac{1}{4}}$.

First simplify numerator and denominator as far as possible.

Numerator $= 3\frac{1}{3} + \frac{5}{4} \times \frac{2}{5} = 3\frac{1}{3} + \frac{1}{2} = 3\frac{5}{6}$

Denominator $= 2\frac{2}{5} - 1\frac{1}{4} = 1 + \frac{2}{5} - \frac{1}{4} = \dfrac{20 + 8 - 5}{20}$

$$= \frac{23}{20}$$

$$\therefore \text{Expression} = 3\frac{5}{6} \div \frac{23}{20} = \frac{\overset{1}{23}}{\underset{3}{6}} \times \frac{\overset{10}{20}}{\underset{1}{23}} = \frac{10}{3}$$

$$= 3\frac{1}{3}.$$

Simplify the following expressions:

1. $\frac{2}{3} + \frac{3}{7} \times 1\frac{2}{5}$

2. $\dfrac{\frac{2}{3} + \frac{3}{4}}{\frac{3}{4} - \frac{2}{3}}$

3. $(2\frac{1}{2} - 1\frac{3}{5}) \div (3\frac{1}{4} + 1\frac{1}{7})$

4. $\dfrac{\frac{3}{5} \times 1\frac{1}{4} - \frac{2}{5}}{1\frac{1}{2} \times 2\frac{1}{3} + 7\frac{7}{8}}$

5. $\frac{7}{8} \times (3\frac{1}{4} - 2\frac{2}{7}) + \frac{1}{2}$

6. $\dfrac{\frac{1}{2} + \frac{2}{5} - \frac{3}{8}}{\frac{1}{2} + \frac{2}{5} + \frac{3}{8}}$

8. Problems

We shall complete the chapter with a few applications to problems.

Ex. 21. Williams, Brown and Higginbottom share a prize of £120. Williams is entitled to one-third of it and Brown gets three-eighths of it. How much money can Higginbottom expect to receive?

Brown and Williams have $\frac{3}{8} + \frac{1}{3}$ of the money

∴ Higginbottom will have $1 - (\frac{3}{8} + \frac{1}{3})$ of it.

$$1 - (\tfrac{3}{8} + \tfrac{1}{3}) = 1 - \frac{9 + 8}{24} = 1 - \tfrac{17}{24}$$

$$= \frac{24 - 17}{24} = \tfrac{7}{24}$$

∴ Higginbottom gets $\frac{7}{24}$ of £120

$$= £\frac{7}{24} \times 120 = \textbf{£35.}$$

Ex. 22. Roberts died and left two-thirds of his estate to his wife; three-quarters of the remainder was willed to his son. If his niece was entitled to the residue, how much did she receive if the estate was valued at £2400?

The wife received $\frac{2}{3}$ of the estate, so $\frac{1}{3}$ remained.

The son received $\frac{3}{4}$ of this remainder, i.e. $\frac{3}{4}$ of $\frac{1}{3}$ = $\frac{1}{4}$ of the estate.

Between them they had $\frac{2}{3} + \frac{1}{4} = \frac{11}{12}$ of the estate.

$\therefore$ The niece received what was left, i.e. $\frac{1}{12}$.

$\therefore$ The niece had $\frac{1}{12}$ of £2400 = **£200.**

EXERCISE 5

1. Express £1 7s. 6d. as a fraction of £3 12s. 6d. in lowest terms.

2. Two-fifths of a sum of money is £2400. How much is three-quarters of it?

3. Brown sold his car for three-fifths of the cost price and finds that in doing so he has lost £250. For how much did he sell the car?

4. The formula for the focal length of a lens is $\dfrac{1}{v} + \dfrac{1}{u} = \dfrac{1}{f}$. Find f if $u = 7$ in., $v = 3$ in.

5. A contractor employs 119 men to build a factory. After 44 days two-thirds of the building is completed. He then employs 35 more men. How long will it take to complete the work?

6. Robinson cycles 2 miles to the station. He takes a train for two-thirds of his journey and a bus for the remaining quarter. How long was his complete journey?

7. Brown can plant his lettuces in an hour and a half. His son could plant them in two and a half hours. How long would it take them if they worked together?

8. Find the cost of $2\frac{3}{8}$ lb. of ham at 5s. 4d. a lb.

CHAPTER FIVE

MONEY

1. The English Coinage

Money tables are included in the tables on page xv. The student will be assumed to be familiar with the tables, but one or two points are worthy of consideration.

£1 = 20s. = 20 × 12d. = 240d. This system possesses one advantage over other possible systems. The number 240 has many different factors and can therefore be divided up into equal-sized parts in many ways.[1] In all other ways the sterling system is greatly inferior to the systems used abroad, e.g. 100 centimes = 1 franc (France), 100 cents = $1 (U.S.A.). The latter currencies merely involve multiplying or dividing by 100 in converting from, say, francs to centimes or dollars to cents (see Chapter 7). Some of the calculations in £ s. d. are long and involved. How much easier it would be if we were to adopt the system 100 pence = £1! Even 10d. = 1s., 10s. = £1 would be a great improvement, the new shilling being worth the same as the present florin (that is, 2s.).

We must, however, accept the coinage as it is.[2]

2. Addition

Everyone is familiar with the type of addition required in making out a bill, so a few examples illustrating methods of procedure will suffice.

[1] The factors of 240 are 1, 2, 3, 4, 5, 6, 8, 10, 12, 15, 16, 20, 24, 30, 40, 48, 60, 80, 120 and 240. Altogether there are 20 of them.
[2] Some colonies, e.g. Cyprus, have recently adopted the coinage 1000 mills = £1. This is similar to the Egyptian system 1000 millièmes = £E1.

39

Ex. 1. s. d.

   4 7   Pence column $7 + 9 + 11 + 8 = 35$

   2 9 $35 \div 12 = 2,$

     11   remainder **11d.**

   1 8   Carry 2 to shillings column

                    $4 + 2 + 1 + 2 = $ **9s.**

  9 11

  2 35

Ex. 2. Add £ s. d.

    3 17 $4\frac{1}{4}$ $\frac{1}{4} + \frac{3}{4} + \frac{1}{2} = 1\frac{1}{2}$d. Put down

      19 $5\frac{3}{4}$ $\frac{1}{2}$d., carry 1

  38 5 $7\frac{1}{2}$ $4 + 5 + 7 + 1 = 17$d.

                $17 \div 12 = 1$, remainder **5d.**,

£43 **2** **$5\frac{1}{2}$d.** carry 1.

  2   1 17 $17 + 19 + 5 + 1 = 42$

              $42 \div 20 = 2$, remainder **2s.**,

              carry 2.

              $3 + 38 + 2 = $ **43.**

3. Subtraction

Ex. 3. Brown has a monthly income of £63 14s. 5d. He spends £59 18s. 8d. How much does he save?

              Borrow 1s. from shillings column.

  £ s. d. $12 + 5 = 17$; $17 - 8 = $ **9d.**

        12   Repay under 18s. making 19s. to

 63 14 5   subtract.

 59 18 8   Borrow £1 from pounds column.

  1 1 $20 + 14 = 34$; $34 - 19 = $ **15s.**

 3 15 **9** Repay under 9; $59 + 1 = 60.$

              $63 - 60 = $ **£3.**

There are several good methods of subtraction. If the student knows one well, he is not advised to change it in working this type of question. (For example, in borrowing as above, we could always subtract from the number borrowed $12 - 8 = 4$; $4 + 5 = 9$d.; and $20 - 19 = 1$; $1 + 14 = 15$s.)

EXERCISE 1

Add together the following:

1.	s.	d.		2.	s.	d.		3.	s.	d.
	2	7½			4	8¼			13	9
		9			7	2½			16	10¾
	5	1			3	0¼			14	8½
	6	3				8			9	3¾

4.	£	s.	d.		5.	£	s.	d.		6.	£	s.	d.
	16	5	8			38	4	9			1034	11	8
	3	16	5½			247	17	11			28	16	4½
	48	0	7½			195	15	7			3	8	9½
											2435	7	10

Subtract the following:

7.	s.	d.		8.	s.	d.		9.	s.	d.
	8	9½			15	4¼			19	1½
	4	10¼			9	7½			16	7¾

10.	£	s.	d.		11.	£	s.	d.		12.	£	s.	d.
	5	4	9			27	6	5½			492	3	6
	3	11	10			19	13	7			395	17	8½

13. Jones bought a new hat for £2 8s. 6d. and a new coat for £14 14s. 8d. How much change did he have out of £20? (Compare Chapter 1, Ex. 9.)

14. Brown sold a carpet for £24 16s. 6d. at a profit of £5 17s. 9d. What did it cost him originally?

4. Reduction

It is often convenient to reduce £ s. d. to pence, and conversely to express a large number of pence in £ s. d. For this purpose the following method should be known. The same method in reducing weights and measures (Chapter 6) is applied, although of course the detailed working differs.

A. – 3

Ex. 4. Reduce £37 15s. 8d. to pence.

The normal method is
```
   37 pounds
   20 ×
  ─────
  740
   15 +
  ─────
  755 shillings
   12 ×
  ─────
  9060
    8 +
  ─────
  9068 pence
```

It can be conveniently laid out as follows, thus saving much space:

£	s.	d.
37	740	9060
	15	8
	755	9068

Multiply pounds by 20, add in shillings: multiply result by 12, add in pence. (£37 = 37 × 20s. = 740s.; 740 + 15 = 755s.; 755s. = 755 × 12d. = 9060d.; 9060 + 8 = 9068d.)

Reduction can further be continued to farthings if required by multiplying by 4, and adding in any farthings present.

The reverse process is clearly illustrated in the example below.

Ex. 5. Express 34,962 farthings in £ s. d.

```
 4)34962
12) 8740 + 2 f. (= ½d.)
20)  728 + 4d.
      36 + 8s.
```
                                    Result **£36 8s. 4½d.**

Dividing by 4 converts the farthings to pence—remainder 2 f. = ½d. appears in answer.

Dividing by 12 converts the pence to shillings—remainder 4d. appears in answer.

Dividing by 20 converts the shillings to pounds—remainder 8s. appears in answer.

Result of division by 20, i.e. £36, also appears in the answer.

As an application of reduction of money consider the following problem.

Ex. 6. How many articles costing 15s. 8½d. each can be bought for £17 5s. 6d.?

s.	d.	halfpence		£	s.	d.	halfpence
15	180	376		17	340	4140	
	8	1			5	6	
	188	377			345	4146	8292

```
377)8292(21              2)375
    754              12)187 + 1 halfpenny
    752                 15 + 7d.
    377
    375
```

Twenty-one articles can be bought and there is 15s. 7½d. change.

We reduce both amounts to halfpence as this is a size which makes them into whole quantities of the same unit (½d.).

EXERCISE 2

Reduce the following to pence:
1. £7 14s. 8d.   2. £16 15s. 10d.   3. £204 9s. 5d.

Reduce to farthings:
4. 14s. 5½d.   5. £2 9s. 7¼d.   6. £87 17s. 4¾d.

Express the following in £ s. d.:
7. 4023 pence   8. 21,998 pence
9. 36,195 halfpence   10. 23,607 halfpence
11. 5977 farthings.   12. 861,425 farthings.

Find the number of articles which can be bought for:
13. £2 7s. 10d. if each costs 1s. 2d.
14. £205 19s. 1½d. if each costs 2s. 7d.
15. £226 10s. 0d. if each costs £1 11s. 5½d.

5. Multiplication

Multiplication of money requires considerable care. Several methods are in use, but the following should suffice. They are based on the recommendations of the Mathematical Association.

(*a*) **Short Multiplication.** This is used when the multiplier is less than 13.

Ex. 7. Multiply £37 14s. 7d. by 8.

£	s.	d.
37	14	7
		8 ×

£301	**16**	**8**

5	4	12)56
296	112	4 + **8**
301	20)116	
	5 + 16	

The layout is the same as for long multiplication. The procedure is clear from the example as each stage is worked in accordance with previous principles outlined. The working beneath the answer can, in the case of short multiplication, soon be reduced to one or two carrying figures, the divisions by 12 and 20 being done mentally. (See Ex. 8 below.)

Ex. 8. Multiply £102 9s. 4½d. by 7.

£	s.	d.
102	9	4½
		7 ×

£717	**5**	**7½**
3	2	3

(*b*) **Multiplication by Factors.** As previously, factorisation is useful when the factors do not exceed 12. We multiply by each factor in turn.

Ex. 9. Find the cost of 54 bicycles at £14 8s. 10d. each.
Now 54 = 9 × 6.
∴ Multiply by 9 and then by 6 (or vice versa).

```
            £    s.  d.
            14   8   10
                      9 ×
            3 3  7
          _____
            129  19  6
                      6 ×
          1 5 5  3
          _____
```
Total cost £779 17 0

(c) **Long Multiplication.** Two methods are important.
The first is called the "Wholesale" or "Top Line"
Method. The method is called "top line" because the
numbers in the top line are used as multipliers. The
second method is "Practice". One or other of these
methods is used when the multiplier does not reduce to
factors all less than 13.

Ex. 10. (Top Line Method). Multiply £35 14s. 9d. by
233.

```
        £              s.            d.
        35             14            9
                                    233 ×
      _____
      £8326           16            9
        171  ←        174 ←    12)2097
        1165          932         174 + 9
        6990          2330
        8326        20)3436
                      171 + 16
```

This can after some practice be abbreviated a little,
by omitting divisors and entering remainders in the
correct space immediately. It makes the working neater
but does not otherwise save much space.

Note that in the above example, the number 233 was
multiplied in turn by 9, 14 and 35; the results were

entered below the answer line and the numbers carried from the preceding columns were added in.

(*d*) **Practice.** Practice has many applications in arithmetic. It consists of expressing a quantity as a set of *aliquot parts*. An aliquot part is an exact divisor of a number.

For example, £7 16s. 4½d. can be expressed in aliquot parts as follows:

$$£7 = 7 \times £1$$
$$10s. = \tfrac{1}{2} \times £1$$
$$5s. = \tfrac{1}{2} \times 10s.$$
$$1s. = \tfrac{1}{5} \times 5s.$$
$$4d. = \tfrac{1}{3} \times 1s.$$
$$\tfrac{1}{2}d. = \tfrac{1}{8} \times 4d.$$

Each line is an exact divisor of the line before (except first and second lines which are easily understood).

Ex. 11. Find by Practice the cost of 79 articles at £16 12s. 5½d. each.

	£	s.	d.
£1	79	0	0
£4	316	0	0
£16	1264	0	0
10s. (= ½ of £1)	39	10	0 (Divide top line by 2)
2s. (= ⅕ of 10s.)	7	18	0
4d. (= ⅙ of 2s.)	1	6	4
1d. (= ¼ of 4d.)		6	7
½d. (= ½ of 1d.)		3	3½
£	1313	4	2½ Total cost.

There are two points to observe about this method.

(1) Avoid choosing too many aliquot parts. The more parts chosen, the greater the chance of error. (For example in the above question, the student might easily have chosen 3d. = ⅛ of 2s.; 1d. = ⅓ of 3d., and again 1d. = ⅓ of 3d. to give a total of 5d., and also incidentally an unnecessary line of working.)

(2) It is a powerful method and well worth the care needed in gaining fluency and precision.

EXERCISE 3

Multiply:

1. £16 4s. 3d. by 7   2. £23 11s. 8d. by 9
3. £204 6s. 4¼d. by 11   4. £1045 17s. 9½d. by 12.

Multiply, using factors:

5. £3 5s. 4d. by 56   6. 16s. 10½d. by 176
7. £64 14s. 10d. by 144   8. £231 19s. 4½d. by 49.

Multiply, by "Top Line" Method:

9. £6 9s. 4d. × 17   10. £11 15s. 7d. × 23
11. £14 9s. 6½d. × 145   12. £62 16s. 7d. × 383.

Find, by Practice, the cost of:

13. 71 tons of coal at £18 19s. 4d. a ton.
14. 107 boxes of apples at 18s. 7½d. a box.
15. 2 gross of drawing instrument sets at £2 15s. 5d. a set.
16. 41 motor cycles at £216 14s. 7d. each.

Find, by any suitable method:

17. The cost of 509 articles at 9s. 5½d. each.
18. The cost of 614 articles at £6 11s. 9d. a dozen.
19. The cost of 1000 pencils at £2 11s. od. a gross.
20. The cost, to the nearest penny, of 100 articles at 3s. 8d. a dozen.

6. Division

We shall consider three methods of division: firstly, short division; secondly, division by factors; and thirdly, long division.

Ex. 12. Divide £24 7s. 1d. by 5.

$$\begin{array}{c c c}
£ & s. & d. \\
 & 80 & 24 \\
\hline
5)24 & 7 & 1 \\
\hline
\end{array}$$

Result **£4 17 5**

The steps are easily seen: 24 ÷ 5 = **4**, r. 4: £4 = 80s.: 80 + 7 = 87s.: 87 ÷ 5 = **17**, r. 2: 2s. = 24d.: 24 + 1 = 25d.: 25 ÷ 5 = **5d.** (r. stands for remainder.)

Ex. 13. Divide £61 13s. 9d. equally among 42 people.
We use the method of factors, as 42 = 7 × 6.

```
        £   s.   d.
           100
     7)61  13    9
            40   24
     6)  8  16    3
        £1   9   4½        Each receives £1 9s. 4½d.
```

The following method of long division is easily
mastered.

Ex. 14. Divide £215 16s. 11d. by 37.

```
        £        s.        d.
        5        16        8
    37)215       16        11      Each part is £5 16s. 8d.
       185    →600      →288      and there is 3d. left over.
        30_|   616         299
               37          296
              246            3
              222
               24_|
```

The pounds are divided as in ordinary long division.
Remainder £30 = 600s.: add in the 16s. in the dividend,
giving 616s. Long division by 37 gives quotient 16s. and
remainder 24s.: 24s. = 288d.: add in 11d.: divide 299d.
by 37: remainder 3d. The quotient appears on top.

EXERCISE 4

Find by short division:

1. £21 5s. 8d. ÷ 4   **2.** £38 15s. 6d. ÷ 11
3. £62 7s. 7d. ÷ 9   **4.** £1045 18s. 6d. ÷ 12.

Find by the method of factors:

5. £14 6s. 6d. ÷ 18   **6.** £1 8s. 5¼d. ÷ 35
7. £780 3s. 0d. ÷ 63   **8.** £200 ÷ 49 (nearest 1d.)

Find by long division:

9. £350 ÷ 17   **10.** £284 6s. 5d. ÷ 29

11. £1045 17s. 11d. ÷ 61   **12.** £1671 5s. 10d. ÷ 87.

13. Jones died and left £686 11s. 9d. He directed that the money should be divided between his wife and two children so that his wife received four times as much as either child, and the children were to get equal shares. How much did he leave his wife?

14. Brown took a party of 38 children to the theatre. The seats cost 6s. 6d. each including his own. How much change did he have from £15?

15. Make out a bill for the following goods purchased and find the total cost.

	£	s.	d.
7 tins of paint at 8s. 3d. a tin			
13 rolls of wallpaper at 16s. 5d. a roll			
14 lb. distemper at 1s. 5½d. a lb.			
3 brushes costing 2s. 9d., 4s. 7d. and 13s. 5d. respectively			

16. What is the cost of motoring 27,547 miles at 4¾d. a mile?

17. What fraction of £5 is 16s. 8d.?

18. Express £2 17s. 9d. as a fraction of £3 15s. 0d. in lowest terms.

CHAPTER SIX

WEIGHTS AND MEASURES

1. Simple Processes

A table of weights and measures is given on page xiii and these should be known. The procedure is similar to that adopted with money, and examples of various types should suffice as explanation.

It is worth noting that in dealing with linear measure, it is customary to use miles, furlongs, chains, yards, feet and inches for most purposes. Now 22 yards = 1 chain, 10 chains = 1 furlong and these give reasonable calculations. If the alternative of $5\frac{1}{2}$ yards = 1 pole, 40 poles = 1 furlong be adopted the results are sometimes curious and the arithmetic is tiresome. Nevertheless, in surveying, such measurements are required. We shall, however, rarely use them in this book.

Towards the end of the chapter more elaborate problems will be discussed, including compound practice.

2. Reduction and the Converse

Ex. 1. Reduce 7 yd. 1 ft. 3 in. to inches.

yd.	ft.	in.
7	21	264
	1	3
	—	—
	22	**267**

Result **267 in.**
(Compare Ch. 4, Ex. 4.)

Ex. 2. Express 8 ton 14 cwt. 3 qr. 9 lb. in lb.

ton	cwt.	qr.	lb.
8	160	696	5592
	14	3	13980
	—	—	9
	174	699	**19,581**

Answer **19,581 lb.**

Ex. 3. Express 2975 pints in quarters, bushels, etc.

$$
\begin{array}{r}
2)\overline{2975} \\
4)\overline{1487} + \textbf{1 pt.} \\
2)\ \overline{\ 371} + \textbf{3 qt.} \\
4)\ \overline{\ 185} + \textbf{1 gall.} \\
8)\ \overline{\ \ 46} + \textbf{1 pk.} \\
\overline{\ \ \ \ 5} + \textbf{6 bush.}
\end{array}
$$

Result **5 qr. 6 bush. 1 pk. 1 gall, 3 qt. 1 pt.**

(Compare Ch. 4, Ex. 5)

It often happens that it is necessary to express one measurement as a fraction of another in simplest form.

Ex. 4. What fraction of 4 days 14 hr. 15 min. is 3 days 17 hr. 15 min.?

$$
\frac{3 \text{ d. 17 hr. 15 min.}}{4 \text{ d. 14 hr. 15 min.}} = \frac{5355 \text{ min.}}{6615 \text{ min.}}
$$

d.	hr.	min.
3	72	5340
	17	15
	89	**5355** min.
4	96	6600
	14	15
	110	**6615** min.

$$
\begin{array}{r}
17 \\
\cancel{119} \\
\cancel{1071} \\
5355 \\
\hline
6615 \\
\cancel{1323} \\
\cancel{147} \\
21 \\
= \dfrac{17}{21}.
\end{array}
$$

We reduce numerator and denominator to the same units (minutes in Ex. 4) and then reduce to lowest terms by removing common factors.

EXERCISE 1

1. Reduce the following to pounds:
  (a) 4 cwt. 3 qr. 9 lb. (b) 1 ton 7 cwt. 0 qr. 23 lb.
  (c) 5 ton 18 cwt. (d) 4 ton 17 cwt. 1 qr. 18 lb.

2. Reduce the following to feet:
    (a) 5 fur. 3 ch. 10 yd. 2 ft.   (b) 2 mi. 5 fur.
    (c) 1 fur. 2 p. 3 yd.   (d) 4 fur. 3 p. 2½ yd.

3. Reduce to pints:
    (a) 1 bush. 3 pk. 1 gall.   (b) 2 qr. 3 bush. 2 pk.

4. Express 1 week in seconds.

5. How many inches are there in 1 mile?

6. Express 3 fur. 10 yd. in inches.

7. Express the following in yards, feet and inches:
    (a) 47 in.   (b) 209 in.   (c) 728 in.

8. Express in miles, furlongs, chains, yards, feet and inches:
    (a) 80,000 in.   (b) 17,448 ft.   (c) 19¼ fur.

9. Express in tons, hundredweights, quarters and pounds:
    (a) 519 lb.   (b) 68,500 oz.   (c) 78,500 lb.

10. Express in days, hours, minutes and seconds:
    (a) 1000 min.   (b) 85,590 sec.   (c) 10^6 sec.

11. Express in quarters, bushels, pecks, etc.:
    (a) 1000 pt.   (b) 2473 pt.   (c) 1487 pt.

12. Find what fraction the smaller quantity is of the greater in each of the following cases, giving the answer in lowest terms:
    (a) 13 min.; 2 hr. 13 min.   (b) 7 oz.; 2 lb. 3 oz.
    (c) 11 yd.; 3 ch.   (d) 2 qt. 1 pt.; 1 gall. 1 qt
    (e) 10 hr. 43 min. 20 sec.; 6 days 16 hr. 50 sec.
    (f) 2 cwt. 0 qr. 21 lb.; 1 ton 5 cwt. 2 qr.

13. A bale of cloth is 27 yd. long. How many curtains 8 ft. 6 in. long can be cut from it and how much is left over?

3. Examples on Addition, Subtraction, Multiplication and Division

Ex. 5. Six passengers embarking in an aircraft were weighed. Their weights were found to be 12 st. 8 lb., 11 st. 9 lb., 8 st. 6 lb., 14 st. 11 lb., 6 st. 7 lb. and 9 st. 9 lb. How many pounds is this?

st.	lb.
12	8
11	9
8	6
14	11
6	7
9	9
63	**8**
3	14)50
	3 + 8

Total weight 63 st. 8 lb.

st.	lb.
63	252
	630
	8
	890

Weight in lb. is 890.

It is easier here to calculate total weight in the units given, before conversion to pounds.

Ex. 6. 34 houses are being built along one side of a road, the frontage of each house being 9 yd. 1 ft. 9 in. How long a stretch of road is needed?

ch.	yd.	ft.	in.
	9	1	9

34× Required length of road

14	17	2	6	14 ch. 17 yd. 2 ft. 6 in.

19	25	12)306	(Compare Ch. 4, Ex. 10)
306	34	25 + **6**	
22)325	3)59		
14 + 17	19 + 2		

Ex. 7. Divide 200 tons by 17.

ton	cwt.	qr.	lb.
11	**15**	**1**	**4**

17)200	0	0	0
17	260	20	84
30)260	)20	)84	(Compare Ch. 4, Ex. 14)
17 17	17	68	
13 90	3	**16 lb.**	
85			
5			

Answer **11 ton, 15 cwt. 1 qr. 4 lb. (remainder 16 lb.)**

These examples show two features:

(i) That the procedure is the same as for handling money problems; only the units are different.

(ii) That the metric system reduces very greatly the complexity of calculation. Children in France have a thorough grasp of the arithmetic of everyday life at a much earlier date than our own, because of the simplicity of their system of decimals.

Time (measured in hours, minutes and seconds) is international, and is intimately linked with navigation. It would not seem that modification would be beneficial in the time scale. Scientists have long recognised the advantages of the metric system, however, and laboratory measurements of length and weight are usually carried out in centimetres and grammes.

The author has noticed, however, that when land is for sale, the agents often give the area as, say 2·14 acres, instead of acres, roods, etc.

EXERCISE 2

1. Add together the following:
  (a) 2 d. 5 hr. 46 min., 3 d. 19 hr. 31 min., 6 hr. 7 min.
  (b) 1 mi. 3 fur. 4 ch. 12 yd., 2 mi. 4 fur. 7 ch. 17 yd.
  (c) 2 bush. 3 pk. 0 gall. 1 qt., 3 pk. 1 gall. 3 qt., 5 bush. 1 pk.

2. Subtract:
  (a) 10 hr. 14 min. 7 sec. from 23 hr. 12 min. 5 sec.
  (b) 14 yd. 2 ft. 3 in. from 21 yd. 1 ft. 1 in.
  (c) 3 mi. 2 fur. 9 ch. 6 yd. from 4 mi.
  (d) 2 ton 17 cwt. 3 qr. 18 lb. from 5 ton 4 cwt.

3. Multiply:
  (a) 5 ch. 7 yd. 2 ft. by 8 (fur. ch. yd. ft.)
  (b) 17 hr. 5 min. 12 sec. by 17 (d. hr. min. sec.)
  (c) 4 lb. 13 oz. by 83 (cwt. qr. lb. oz.)
  (d) 7 dwt. 14 gr. by 28 (oz. dwt. gr.).

4. Divide:
  (a) 4 ton 8 cwt. 3 qr. by 7 (cwt. qr. lb.)
  (b) 6 d. 7 hr. by 23 (hr. min. sec.)
  (c) 2 mi. 5 fur. 6 ch. by 89 (yd. ft. in.).

5. In a factory employing 140 men, each man averages 7 hr. 38 min. a day. How many hours of work are done each week?

6. How many minutes are there between 6.42 a m. on 2nd November 1960 and 9.27 p.m. on 3rd November 1960?

7. Brown & Co., Coal Merchants, have 15 tons of anthracite in stock. They deliver orders as follows: 17 cwt., 5 cwt., 3 cwt., 3 ton 6 cwt., 5 cwt., 8 cwt., 1½ ton, 4 cwt. to 8 customers. How much anthracite is left in stock, and what is the average amount that each customer takes? (To find the average, take the total amount delivered and divide by the number of customers.)

8. A lorry is weighed on a weighbridge and found to be 3 ton 5 cwt. 1 qr. when loaded with 28 packing cases each of 100 lb. weight. Find the unladen weight of the lorry.

4. Compound Practice

The reader who is not familiar with simple decimals is advised to read Chapter 7, sections 1 and 2, before studying this section.

In Chapter 5 we saw how to find the cost of a number of articles by simple practice. We now extend the method to the case when we have to multiply two compound quantities together.

Ex. 8. Find the cost of 5 ton 6 cwt. 1 qr. at £17 9s. 4d. a ton.

	£	s.	d.
Cost of 1 ton	17	9	4
Cost of 5 ton	87	6	8
Cost of 4 cwt. (= ⅕ of 1 ton)	3	9	10·4
Cost of 2 cwt. (= ½ of 4 cwt.)	1	14	11·2
Cost of 1 qr. (= ⅛ of 2 cwt.)		4	4·4
	92	15	10·0

Total cost **£92 15s. 10d.**

In this example it should be noticed that the pence are worked in decimals. This is undoubtedly the best way.

Normally *two places of decimals are used and the answer is corrected to the nearest penny* (e.g. 3·18d. is taken as 3d.; 4·63d. is taken as 5d.).

It is possible to work multiplication of two compound quantities by expressing both as decimals, multiplying, and converting the result back to the original units. The method is not advocated as it tends to be long and tedious.

EXERCISE 3

1. Find the cost of 27 jars of marmalade at 1s. 10½d. a jar.

2. Find the cost of 8¼ lb. of bacon at 4s. 9d. a lb.

3. What is the cost of 7 yd. 2 ft. 9 in. of material at £1 7s. 3d. a yard?

4. How much would 274 yd. of cable cost at 1s. 4½d. a foot?

5. A farmer buys the crop growing on a field at £7 16s. 8d. an acre. How much would it cost him to buy the crop on a field of area 17 ac. 3 r. 7 sq. p.? (To the nearest 1d.)

6. Find the cost of 8 ton 7 cwt. 3 qr. coal at £19 9s. 2d. a ton. (To the nearest 1d.)

7. An insurance agent is paid 3s. 6d. in every £1 which he gets in orders for the manufacture of cosmetics. How much will he be paid for orders of £287?

CHAPTER SEVEN

DECIMALS—THE METRIC SYSTEM

1. Introduction

We have seen that fractions consist of quantities like $\frac{3}{4}$, $\frac{5}{19}$ and $\frac{7}{2}$, and that they are cumbersome to handle, because simplification entails bringing them to the same denominator or some other fairly elaborate manipulation. A simpler process, involving uniform denominators, is clearly often desirable.

The system of *numbers* we use is the decimal scale (i.e. scale of 10). The numbers read 1, 10, 100, 1000 and so on. This suggests an extension

$$\leftarrow 1000,\ 100,\ 10,\ 1,\ \tfrac{1}{10},\ \tfrac{1}{100},\ \tfrac{1}{1000} \rightarrow$$

so that the terms on the left of 1 are obtained by successive multiplication by ten, and those on the right by successive division by ten. We can, if we wish, rewrite the sequence above as

$$\leftarrow 10^3,\ 10^2,\ 10,\ 1,\ \tfrac{1}{10},\ \tfrac{1}{10^2},\ \tfrac{1}{10^3} \rightarrow$$

that is, as *powers* of ten. The fractions on the right all have powers of ten as denominators. They are called *decimals*, so a decimal is defined as *a fraction whose denominator is some power of ten*.

We greatly simplify working with decimals by adopting the following notation:

$$(\text{1 tenth})\ \tfrac{1}{10} = \cdot 1;\quad (\text{1 hundredth})\ \tfrac{1}{100} = \cdot 01;$$
$$(\text{3 hundredths})\ \tfrac{3}{100} = \cdot 03;$$
$$(\text{17 thousandths})\ \tfrac{17}{1000} = \cdot 017.$$

Ex. 1. Express the following as decimals:

(a) $4 + \frac{8}{100}$ (b) $20 + 8 + \frac{7}{10}$

(c) $3 \times 10^4 + 2 \times 10^2 + 4 \times 10$ (d) $\frac{6}{10} + \frac{5}{100}$

(e) $74.905 + \frac{87}{1000}$ (f) $\frac{3}{1000}$.

The results have been laid out in tabular form so as to illustrate clearly the various points to bear in mind. It is quite unnecessary to adopt this method in working examples once the principles are understood.

	10^4	10^3	10^2	10	I	$\frac{1}{10}$	$\frac{1}{10^2}$	$\frac{1}{10^3}$	
	Ten-thousands	Thousands	Hundreds	Tens	Units	Tenths	Hundredths	Thousandths	Answers
(a)					4		8		4·08
(b)				2	8	7			28·7
(c)	3		2	4					30240
(d)						6	5		0·65
(e)	7	4	9		5		8	7	74905·087
(f)								3	0·003

Notes

1. We put in noughts to fill gaps in the results.

2. In (c) above, the number was written in powers of ten to show that it can be dealt with as a decimal.

3. Note that in (e), $\frac{87}{1000}$ is the same as $\frac{80}{1000} + \frac{7}{1000} = \frac{8}{100} + \frac{7}{1000}$.

4. In (d) and (f) where there is no whole number in front of the decimal point, we put in a 0.

5. Figures in the tenths, hundredths, thousandths etc. columns are called figures in the first, second, third etc. decimal place.

2. Addition and Subtraction

We use the decimal point as our guide in putting down numbers to be added or subtracted in columns.

Ex. 2. Add together 72·95, 2·0604, 319·5, 204.

$$72 \cdot 95$$
$$2 \cdot 0604$$
$$319 \cdot 5$$
$$204$$

598·5104

The carrying figures are taken from column to column in the ordinary way (as in Chapter 1). The presence of the decimal point does not affect the procedure.

Ex. 3. Subtract 4·0805 from 9·1.

$$9 \cdot 1000$$
$$4 \cdot 0805$$

5·0195

Here, unlike addition, it is best to put in the missing zeros (9·1 is the same as 9·1000).

EXERCISE 1

1. Express the following as decimals:

   (a) $2 + \frac{3}{10}$ (b) $6 + \frac{1}{100}$ (c) $30 + 7 + \frac{5}{10} + \frac{7}{100}$

   (d) $\frac{9}{10} + \frac{1}{100}$ (e) $\frac{7}{100}$ (f) $\frac{4}{10000}$

   (g) $80 + 5 + \frac{7}{100} + \frac{6}{1000}$.

2. Write out the following decimals as the sum of decimal fractions (e.g. $2 \cdot 04 = 2 + \frac{4}{100}$):

   (a) 6·8   (b) 14·92   (c) 207·04

   (d) 0·6   (e) 0·094   (f) 1000·001.

3. Add together

   (a) 26·48, 3·9, 0·882

   (b) 300·7, 0·006, 29·908

   (c) 217·85, 86·57, 1709·08

   (d) 2·0064, 693·907, 0·087, 774·8.

4. Subtract:

   (a) 38·7 from 62·4   (b) 3·95 from 17·7

   (c) 0·927 from 10   (d) 904·767 from 1202·6825.

3. Multiplication and Division—Introduction

Multiplying by 10 merely necessitates moving the decimal point *one place to the right*.

E.g. $4 \cdot 37 \times 10 = 43 \cdot 7$ (because $[4 + \frac{3}{10} + \frac{7}{100}] \times 10$
$$= 40 + 3 + \frac{7}{10} = 43 \cdot 7).$$

Dividing by 10 is carried out by moving the decimal point *one place to the left.*

E.g. $9 \cdot 2 \div 10 = 0 \cdot 92$ (because $[9 + \frac{2}{10}] \div 10$
$$= \frac{9}{10} + \frac{2}{100} = 0 \cdot 92).$$

This rule can be generalised as follows:

To multiply by 10, 100, 1000 etc., move the decimal point 1, 2, 3 etc. places to the right.

To divide by 10, 100, 1000 etc., move the decimal point, 1, 2, 3 etc. places to the left.

E.g. $62 \cdot 5 \times 1000 = 62500$
$$62 \cdot 5 \div 1000 = 0 \cdot 0625.$$

Multiplication and division in general are carried out in much the same way as with ordinary numbers in Chapter 1. Care must be taken to see that the decimal point is kept in the correct position.

This is easily effected by noting the total number of decimal places present and putting the decimal point in front of them.

Consider $0 \cdot 035 \times 3$.

We have $35 \times 3 = 105$

i.e. $0 \cdot 035 \times 3 = \mathbf{0 \cdot 105}$ (as there are 3 decimal places).

We can check this as follows:

$$0 \cdot 035 \times 3 = \frac{35}{1000} \times 3 = \frac{105}{1000} = \mathbf{0 \cdot 105}.$$

Ex. 4. $0 \cdot 7 \times 3 = \mathbf{2 \cdot 1}$ $[0 \cdot 7 \times 3 = \frac{7}{10} \times 3 = \frac{21}{10} = 2 \cdot 1]$.

Ex. 5. $21 \cdot 6 \times 7 = \mathbf{151 \cdot 2}$.

Ex. 6. $0 \cdot 0984 \times 6 = \mathbf{0 \cdot 5904}$.

Ex. 7. $0 \cdot 0042 \times 5 = 0 \cdot 0210 = \mathbf{0 \cdot 021}$.

Although we get $0 \cdot 0210$, *eventually* the final zero is not put down as it does not affect the value of the answer.

4. Multiplication

When decimals appear in both the multiplicand and the multiplier:

(a) Multiply the numbers as though they were whole.
(b) Determine the position of the decimal point in the
answer by finding the total number of decimal places.

Ex. 8. $0.073 \times 0.1 = \mathbf{0.0073}$
$\qquad (3 + 1 = 4 \text{ decimal places}).$

Ex. 9. Find the value of 23.58×17.5.

Use the rules above.

```
    2358
     175 ×
   _____
   11790    2 + 1 = 3 decimal places.
   16506    Result 412·650; we then omit the final
    2358    zero when writing the answer, but not
   _____    before.
  412650
```

$\therefore 23.58 \times 17.5 = \mathbf{412.65}.$

Although the above is undoubtedly the simplest
method and also the safest, it is not suitable when con-
tracted multiplication is required (i.e. when several of
the figures in the answer are superfluous).

Multiplication by factors can often be carried out, but
it is rarely of value. (Division by factors is, on the other
hand, important.)

As a final example of multiplication of the normal type
consider:

Ex. 10. $36{,}000 \times 0.01835$ $\qquad$ 1835
$\qquad = 36 \times 18.35$ $\qquad\qquad\quad$ 36 ×
$\qquad\qquad\qquad\qquad\qquad\qquad\qquad$ _____
$\qquad = \mathbf{660.6}.$ $\qquad\qquad\qquad\qquad$ 11010
$\qquad\qquad\qquad\qquad\qquad\qquad\qquad$ 5505
$\qquad\qquad\qquad\qquad\qquad\qquad\qquad$ _____
$\qquad\qquad\qquad\qquad\qquad\qquad\qquad$ **66060**

[We divide 36,000 by 1000, thus removing the zeros;
we multiply 0.01835 by 1000, so compensating. The result is considerable simplification.

Otherwise we can proceed as follows:

$36000 \times 1835 = 1835000 \times 36 = 66060000$

5 d.p. leave $660·60000 = \mathbf{660·6}$, but this is clumsy.

We always multiply by the number which has fewer figures in it; i.e. by 36, not by 1835.]

5. Division

There are numerous methods of division in use, but, for the student practising alone, the following are sufficient.

Ex. 11. Divide 21·7 by 0·0014.

$$\frac{21·7}{·0014} = \frac{217000}{14}$$

$$= \mathbf{15,500}$$

$$\begin{array}{r} 7)\overline{217000} \\ 2)\overline{31000} \\ \hline \mathbf{15500.} \end{array}$$

We *multiply* the top and bottom by the same power of 10 (in this case, we multiply by 10000) to make the divisor a whole number; i.e. we move the decimal point *the same number of places to the right* in the numerator and denominator.

Ex. 12. Divide 380·64 by 2400.

$$\frac{380·64}{2400} = \frac{3·8064}{24}$$

$$= \mathbf{0·1586}$$

$$\begin{array}{r} 6)\overline{3·8064} \\ 4)\overline{0·6344} \\ \hline \mathbf{0·1586} \end{array}$$

Here we *divide* the top and bottom by the same power of 10 to simplify the working; i.e. we move the decimal point *the same number of places to the left* in the numerator and denominator.

It often happens that an exact answer cannot be obtained, or, even if it can be obtained, that it contains more decimal places than we need for our purposes. In such a case we approximate our answer to the degree of accuracy we require. Consider the following example.

Ex. 13. Find the value of $0·0867 \div 0·21$.

$$\frac{0·0867}{0·21} = \frac{8·67}{21}$$

$$= 0·412\ldots$$

$$\backsimeq \mathbf{0·41}$$

$$\begin{array}{r} 7)\overline{8·670} \\ 3)\overline{1·238\ldots} \\ \hline \mathbf{0·412\ldots} \end{array}$$

(The symbol $\frown$ means "is approximately equal to".)

What we have done is to work out the question to 3 places of decimals and we then corrected the answer to an accuracy of 2 decimal places (2 d.p.).

If we had wanted the answer correct to 3 d.p. we would have worked a little farther:

$$
\begin{array}{r}
7)\overline{8 \cdot 6700} \\
3)\overline{1 \cdot 2385\ldots} \\
\hline
\mathbf{0 \cdot 4128}\ldots
\end{array}
$$

and we would have found that $\dfrac{0 \cdot 0867}{0 \cdot 21} \frown \mathbf{0 \cdot 413}$ (3 d.p.).

We take the value 0·413 because 0·4128 lies between 0·412 and 0·413, and *is nearer to the latter.*

One case merits particular attention. What do we take if the last figure is a 5 and we wish to approximate?

E.g. 0·6025 might be 0·602 or 0·603 (to 3 d.p.).

We merely take a convention to go to the higher number, i.e.:

$$0 \cdot 6025 \frown 0 \cdot 603 \text{ (correct to 3 decimal places).}$$

In all of the examples 11–13, we were able to divide by factors. We now have to study long division. As before, we shall make the divisor a whole number.

Ex. 14. Divide 3·8 by 0·89 and give the answer correct to 2 d.p.

$$
\begin{aligned}
\frac{3 \cdot 8}{0 \cdot 89} &= \frac{380}{89} \\
&= 4 \cdot 269\ldots \\
&\frown \mathbf{4 \cdot 27} \text{ (2 d.p.)}
\end{aligned}
$$

$$
\begin{array}{r}
\mathbf{4 \cdot 269} \\
89)\overline{380 \cdot 000} \\
\underline{356} \\
24 \cdot 0 \\
\underline{17 \cdot 8} \\
6 \cdot 20 \\
\underline{5 \cdot 34} \\
860 \\
\underline{801}
\end{array}
$$

Notice that the quotient is written over the dividend

so that the quotient decimal point comes over the dividend decimal point.

It will be observed that in Examples 13 and 14 we introduce zeros as necessary in the dividend. They do not affect its value.

In Ex. 14 we write 380 as 380·000, introducing the decimal point and as many zeros as we need in the working. $380 \div 89 = 4$, remainder 24. Bring down the first decimal place figure, i.e. 0, *and enter the decimal point in the quotient.* $240 \div 89 = 2$, remainder 62, etc. If we write the quotient over the dividend we see clearly where the decimal point will lie.

In the above work we have approximated to a specified number of *places of decimals.* We sometimes require an answer correct to a particular number of *significant figures.* To understand the meaning of significant figures (or significant digits, as they may more accurately be called) requires care.

Digits are the numbers 0, 1, 2, 3, . . ., 9, i.e. the positive whole numbers less than 10, together with zero. Significant digits, or significant figures, are the digits of a number beginning with the first digit on the left which is not zero and ending with the last digit on the right which is not zero. Some illustrations will help the reader to understand this.

$$3608 \text{ has } 4 \text{ significant figures}$$
$$3600 \text{ ,, } 2 \qquad ,, \qquad\qquad ,,$$
$$0·045 \text{ ,, } 2 \qquad ,, \qquad\qquad ,,$$
$$10800 \text{ ,, } 3 \qquad ,, \qquad\qquad ,,$$
$$0·1453 \text{ ,, } 4 \qquad ,, \qquad\qquad ,,$$

The value of 0·4277 correct to 2 significant figures (2 s.f.) is 0·43.

$$\text{Likewise } 4315 \simeq 4300 \text{ (2 s.f.)}$$
$$4360 \simeq 4400 \text{ (2 s.f.).}$$

Note that there are cases where end zeros may be significant

$$21·76963 \simeq 21·770 \text{ (5 s.f.)}$$

(for 0·76963 is nearer 0·770 than 0·769).

EXERCISE 2

Write down the following numbers correct to the accuracy required:

1. 417·3 (3 s.f.)

2. 0·0868 (3 d.p.)

3. 22·0097 (3 d.p.)

4. 6·089 (2 s.f.)

5. 0·006993 (4 d.p.)

6. 0·03087 (3 s.f.)

7. 9·84305 (3 s.f.)

8. 0·0984 (3 d.p.).

Ex. 15. Calculate 0·324 ÷ 72·5 to 3 significant figures.

$$\frac{0·324}{72·5} = \frac{3·24}{725}$$

$$= 0·004468\ldots$$

$$= \mathbf{0·00447}\ \text{(3 s.f.)}$$

```
              0·004468
         725 │ 3·240000
               2·900
               3400
               2900
               5000
               4350
               6500
               5800
```

725 will not divide into 3; put in decimal (0·). It will not divide into 3·2; put in 0·0. It will not divide into 3·24; put in 0·00. It *will* divide into 3·240; enter first significant figure, 4.

EXERCISE 3

1. Find the value of:

  (a) 0·04 × 10   (b) 0·63 × 100   (c) 3·85 × 1000
  (d) 0·007 × 1000 (e) 0·05 × 3   (f) 0·59 × 12
  (g) 0·08 × 20   (h) 1·64 × 300   (i) 0·042 × 120
  (j) 28·9 × 70   (k) 2·024 × 110   (l) 0·53 × $\frac{1}{100}$.

2. Find the value of:

  (a) 6·8 ÷ 2   (b) 5·8 ÷ 4   (c) 3·25 ÷ 10
  (d) 0·08 ÷ 100   (e) 3·84 ÷ 20   (f) 79·8 ÷ 70
  (g) 0·0965 ÷ 0·5 (h) 0·825 ÷ 0·15   (i) 297 ÷ 0·055
  (j) 1·62 ÷ 0·009 (k) 0·14608 ÷ 40   (l) 0·283 ÷ $\frac{1}{100}$.

3. Find the value of the following exactly, unless otherwise stated:

  (a) 24·7 × 3·8   (b) 6·8 × 0·042
  (c) 386·2 × 0·072   (d) 8500 × 0·00132

A. – 4

   (e) $79 \cdot 7 \times 31 \cdot 4$ (2 s.f.)   (f) $8304 \times 0 \cdot 061$ (3 s.f.)
   (g) $8200 \times 0 \cdot 439$ (h) $9070 \times 0 \cdot 00194$ (4 s.f.)
          (i) $0 \cdot 23 \times 61 \cdot 86$ (2 d.p.).

4. Find the value of the following, correct to the accuracy named:
   (a) $29 \cdot 4 \div 33$ (2 d.p.)   (b) $3 \cdot 046 \div 42$ (3 d.p.)
   (c) $0 \cdot 987 \div 0 \cdot 71$ (3 s.f.)   (d) $20 \cdot 45 \div 0 \cdot 93$ (3 s.f.)
   (e) $6 \cdot 4 \div 760$ (4 d.p.)   (f) $39 \cdot 84 \div 1 \cdot 773$ (3 d.p.).

6. Fractions and Decimals

Some fractions can be expressed as exact decimals.

$\frac{1}{2} = 0 \cdot 5$, $\frac{1}{4} = 0 \cdot 25$, $\frac{1}{8} = 0 \cdot 125$.

$\frac{3}{4} = 3 \times \frac{1}{4} = 3 \times 0 \cdot 25 = 0 \cdot 75$ and so on.

Others, however, cannot.

$\frac{1}{3} = 0 \cdot 333 \ldots$

Ex. 16. Express $\frac{3}{7}$ as a decimal to 3 places.

$\frac{3}{7} \simeq \mathbf{0 \cdot 429}$

The reverse process is easily mastered.

Ex. 17. Express $0 \cdot 16$ as a fraction in lowest terms.

$$0 \cdot 16 = \frac{16}{100} = \frac{\overset{4}{\cancel{16}}}{\underset{25}{\cancel{100}}} = \frac{4}{25}.$$

7. Decimalisation of Money

It is of help in calculation to reduce £ s. d. to decimals of £1 on many occasions and in this connection the following relationships are worth remembering.

10s.	= £0·5	1s.	= £0·05
5s.	= £0·25	6d.	= £0·025
2s. 6d.	= £0·125	3d.	= £0·0125
2s.	= £0·1	1½d.	= £0·00625

They are easily obtained; for example:

$$\frac{\text{2s. 6d.}}{£1} = \frac{5 \text{ sixpences}}{40 \text{ sixpences}} = \tfrac{5}{40} = \tfrac{1}{8} = 0\cdot125.$$

Ex. 18. Reduce £8 7s. 4d. to a decimal of £1, correct to 5 significant figures.

$$\begin{array}{r} 12)\underline{4}\cdot00000 \\ 20)\overline{7}\cdot33333\ldots \\ \overline{8\cdot36666\ldots} \end{array}$$

£8 7s. 4d. $\frown$ **£8·3667** (correct to 5 sig. figs.).
The method is neat and easily understood. Divide 4d. by 12, giving ·33333...; add in the 7s. (underlined); divide 7·33333... by 20, giving ·36666...; add in the £8, giving 8·36666....
This method is applicable exactly to weights and measures in general.

Ex. 19. Express 17s. 2½d. as a decimal of £4 correct to 5 decimal places.

$$\frac{\text{17s. 2½d.}}{£4} \frown \mathbf{0\cdot21510} \text{ (5 d.p.)} \qquad \begin{array}{r} 12)\ \underline{2}\cdot5000\ (2\tfrac{1}{2}\text{d.} = 2\cdot5\text{ d.}) \\ 20)\overline{17}\cdot208333\ldots \\ 4)\ \overline{0\cdot8604166\ldots} \\ \overline{0\cdot215104\ldots.} \end{array}$$

Note that the final zero is kept as it is required that answer be given to **5** d.p.
To convert from decimals of a £ to £ s. d. is equally simple.

Ex. 20. Convert £3·81472 to £ s. d. to the nearest 1d.

$$£3\cdot81472 = \mathbf{£3\ 16s.\ 4d.} \qquad \begin{array}{r} 3\cdot81472\ (\times\ 20) \\ \overline{16\cdot2944}\ (\times\ 12) \\ \overline{3\cdot5328} \end{array}$$

We remove the £'s, i.e. £3 above, and multiply the remainder by 20, making it shillings; remove the shillings, i.e. 16s. above, and multiply the remainder by 12, making it pence; approximate to nearest whole 1d.

EXERCISE 4

1. Express the following fractions as decimals, **exactly** where possible, but to four decimal places otherwise:

   (a) $\frac{3}{5}$ (b) $\frac{5}{8}$ (c) $\frac{7}{11}$ (d) $\frac{2}{9}$ (e) $\frac{7}{18}$ (f) $\frac{9}{17}$.

2. Convert the following decimals to vulgar fractions in lowest terms:

   (a) 0·12 (b) 0·716 (c) 0·085 (d) 0·0906 (e) 7·1625.

3. Express the following fractions as decimals correct to three places and hence arrange them in ascending order of magnitude: $\frac{171}{50}$, $\frac{147}{43}$, $\frac{427}{125}$.

4. Reduce the following to decimals of £1, correct to four decimal places:

   (a) £7 12s. 8d. (b) £16 5s. 2½d. (c) £203 17s. 10¼d.

5. Reduce the following to decimals of £ correct to the specified number of decimal places:

   (a) £2 19s. 5d. (3 d.p.)   (b) 18s. 10½d. (5 d.p.)
   (c) £61 18s. 2d. (5 d.p.).

6. Convert the following to £ s. d., to the nearest 1d.:

   (a) £21·74 (b) £0·687 (c) £0·2154 (d) £7·7079.

7. Find the value of 0·36 of £2 15s. 4d.

8. The Metric System

The metric system uses a single *standard measure* for each of length, area, volume and weight. All other measures are obtained from the standards by inserting Latin or Greek prefixes before them.

Length. The unit of length is the *metre*. It is a little more than a yard. 1 metre (m.) = 39·37 in.

Other lengths are obtained as follows:

10 metres	= 1 *deka*metre (Dm.)
100 metres	= 1 *hecto*metre (Hm.)
1000 metres	= 1 *kilo*metre (Km.)
0·1 metre	= 1 *deci*metre (dm.)
0·01 metre	= 1 *centi*metre (cm.)
0·001 metre	= 1 *milli*metre (mm.)

The same prefixes are used for the measures of area, volume and weight.

It will be noticed that 10 mm. = 1 cm.

$$1000 \text{ mm.} = 1 \text{ m.}$$
$$100 \text{ cm.} = 1 \text{ m.}$$
$$100000 \text{ cm.} = 1 \text{ Km. etc.}$$

The kilometre is important and is used in measuring distances between places on the Continent of Europe. The centimetre is widely used in scientific work.

$$1 \text{ Km.} = 1000 \text{ m.}$$
$$= 1000 \times 39 \cdot 37 \text{ in.}$$
$$= \frac{39370}{63360} \text{ mi.}$$
$$\frown \tfrac{5}{8} \text{ mi.}$$

To check that this approximation is justifiable for many practical purposes, we have

$\tfrac{5}{8}$ mile $= \tfrac{5}{8} \times 63360$ in. $= 39600$ in.

and 1 Km. $= 1000 \times 39 \cdot 37$ in. $= \underline{39370}$ in.

The difference between them is $\quad \overline{230}$ in. $\frown$ **19 ft.**

Area. The unit of area is the *square metre*, which is the area of a square of side one metre.

$$\therefore 1 \text{ sq. m.} = 10 \text{ dm.} \times 10 \text{ dm.}$$
$$= 100 \text{ sq. dm.}$$

and so we can build up the following table

100 sq. m.	= 1 sq. Dm.
10000 sq. m.	= 1 sq. Hm.
1000000 sq. m.	= 1 sq. Km.
0·01 sq. m.	= 1 sq. dm.
0·0001 sq. m.	= 1 sq. cm.
0·000001 sq. m.	= 1 sq. mm.

This gives such results as

$$1 \text{ sq. Dm.} = 1000 \text{ cm.} \times 1000 \text{ cm.}$$
$$= \textbf{1000000 sq. cm.}$$

The index notation is often neater in such cases, e.g.

$$1 \text{ sq. Km.} = 10^5 \text{ cm.} \times 10^5 \text{ cm.}$$
$$= \mathbf{10^{10} \text{ sq. cm.}}$$

The square dekametre is called the are (pronounced
AIR).

(i.e. 1 are = 1 sq. Dm. = 100 sq. m.)
and 100 ares = 1 hectare (Ha.)

An area of 1 hectare is about $2\frac{1}{2}$ acres.

Volume. The unit of volume is the *cubic metre*, which
is the volume of a cube of side one metre.

1 cu. m. = 100 cm. × 100 cm. × 100 cm.
= 1000000 cu. cm.

The cubic centimetre is usually written c.c. for short,
rather than cu. cm.

We can build up a table of volumes, which is here
restricted to more usual parts:

1000 (= 10^3) cu. dm. = 1 cu. m.
1000000 (= 10^6) cu. cm. = 1 cu. m.

A volume of 1000 c.c. is called a *litre* (l.). This is the
same as a cubic decimetre. (10 litres = 1 *deka*litre (Dl.)
etc. but we shall only use the, commoner, litre in this
book.)

Weight. The unit of weight is the gramme (gm.) and
it is the weight of one cubic centimetre of water. (The
exact scientific definition is rather more precise.)

Once again a table is devised:

10 gm.   = 1 *deka*gramme (Dg.)
100 gm.   = 1 *hecto*gramme (Hg.)
1000 gm.   = 1 *kilo*gramme (Kg.)
0·1 gm.   = 1 *deci*gramme (dg.)
0·01 gm.   = 1 *centi*gramme (cg.)
0·001 gm.   = 1 *milli*gramme (mg.)

Of these the important ones are kilogramme, gramme
and milligramme. Weights are normally given in terms
of one unit only in the metric system, kilogrammes if
heavy (e.g. 52·83 Kg.), or grammes if light (e.g. 28·6 gm.).

Relationships between English and Metric Systems

A few relationships are worth remembering:

1 in.	= 2·540 cm.	1 cm.	= 0·3937 in.
1 mile	= 1·609 Km.	1 Km.	= 0·6214 mile
1 lb.	= 0·4536 Kg.	1 Kg.	= 2·205 lb.
1 gallon	= 4·546 litres	1 litre	= 1·76 pints.

Ex. 21. Calculate the area of a rectangle, 1 ft. 3 in. by 2 ft. 4 in., in sq. cm.

$$1 \text{ ft. 3 in.} = 15 \text{ in.} = 15 \times 2.54 \text{ cm.}$$
$$2 \text{ ft. 4 in.} = 28 \text{ in.} = 28 \times 2.54 \text{ cm.}$$
$$\therefore \text{Reqd. area} = 15 \times 28 \times (2.54)^2 \text{ sq. cm.}$$
$$= \textbf{2710 sq. cm.} \text{ (nearest sq. cm.).}$$

Ex. 22. Find the weight in lb. of 2·5 litres of water.

$$2.5 \text{ litres} = 2.5 \times 1000 \text{ c.c.} = 2500 \text{ c.c.}$$
and as 1 c.c. of water weighs 1 gm
$$\therefore 2.5 \text{ litres weigh } 2500 \text{ gm., i.e. } 2.5 \text{ Kg.}$$
$$\therefore 2.5 \text{ litres weigh } 2.5 \times 2.205 \text{ lb.}$$
$$\text{i.e. } \textbf{5·51 lb.} \text{ (3 s.f.).}$$

9. Money

Decimal coinage is rapidly becoming the normal currency in most countries in the world. Two principal coinages are:

$$100 \text{ centimes (c.)} = 1 \text{ franc (fr.)}$$
$$100 \text{ cents (c.)} = 1 \text{ dollar ($).}$$

There are other schemes. Cyprus recently replaced 180 piastres to the £ by a new currency, 1000 mils = £1. Egypt has for many years used 1000 millièmes = £E1.

Ex. 23. Find the cost of potatoes in francs per kilogramme, if their price is 2¼d. per lb., given that 980 fr. = £1.

$$1d. = \tfrac{1}{240} \text{ of } £1 = \tfrac{980}{240} \text{ fr.}$$
$$1 \text{ lb.} = 0.4536 \text{ Kg.}$$

$$\therefore \frac{2\frac{1}{4}\text{d.}}{1\text{ lb.}} = \frac{2\frac{1}{4} \times \frac{980}{240}\text{ fr.}}{0\cdot4536\text{ Kg.}} = \frac{\overset{3}{\cancel{9}}}{\underset{4}{\cancel{4}}} \times \frac{\overset{7}{\cancel{49}}}{\underset{\cancel{12}}{\cancel{12}}} \times \frac{1}{\underset{0\cdot0648}{0\cdot4536}}.$$

$$= \frac{21}{1\cdot0368}\text{ fr. per Kg.} = 20\cdot26 \frown \textbf{20 fr. per Kg.}$$

Later we shall see how much easier this kind of calculation is using logarithms.

EXERCISE 5

1. Find the length of a path 30 ft. 8 in. in metres, correct to 3 significant figures.

2. How long is 164 Km. in miles and yards? (1 Km. = 0·6214 mi.)

3. Find the value of (a) $\dfrac{2\cdot5 \times 0\cdot64}{40}$ (b) $\dfrac{0\cdot063 \times 7\cdot8}{0\cdot0091}$.

4. Find the weight in pounds of 1 gall. of water, given that 1 gall. = 4·546 litres and that 1 Kg. = 2·205 lb. Give the answer to 3 significant figures?

5. Find in metres the difference in distance between 5 mi. and 8 Km. (1 mi. = 1·609 Km.)

6. A car is travelling at 85 Km. per hour. How fast is this in miles per hour?

7. What is the volume of a brick 9 in. by $4\frac{1}{2}$ in. by 3 in. in cubic centimetres (correct to 3 significant figures)?

8. A field is 80 metres long and 64 metres wide. Find its area (a) in ares (square dekametres), (b) as a decimal of a hectare.

9. Prove that 1 acre is approximately 0·4 hectare, *without* assuming the statement in the text that 1 hectare $\frown$ 2·5 acres. (1 m. = 39·37 in.)

10. Find the cost, in shillings and pence per lb., of meat which costs 483 francs per kilogram. (Rate of exchange is 973 fr. = £1.)

CHAPTER EIGHT

RATIO, PROPORTION, AVERAGES AND MIXTURES

1. Ratio

Suppose Mr. and Mrs. Barnett wish to buy a house and they see two which appeal to them. The first costs £2400 and the second costs £2800. We say that the *ratio* of the cost price of the first house to that of the second house is as £2400 is to £2800. This can be written:

$$\frac{\text{Cost price of first house}}{\text{Cost price of second house}} = \frac{2400}{2800}$$

$$= \frac{6}{7}, \textit{ in lowest terms.}$$

Another way of writing this is "the ratio of the prices is 6:7." It is important that the numbers are put in the correct order. It will be seen that the £ signs on the right have been removed. This can always be done if the quantities, top and bottom, are the same. We have already used this idea in Chapter 5.

NOTE "6:7" is read "*as six is to* seven".

Ex. 1. Osborn works 40 hours a week. Find the ratio of the time he works to the time when he is not working.

Time working = 40 hr.
Number of hours in a week = 7 × 24 = 168 hr.
∴ Time not working = 168 − 40 = 128 hr.
∴ Required ratio = 40:128
= **5:16.**

Ex. 2. Petrol has been increased in price from 4s. 7½d. to 6s. 0½d. per gall. In what ratio has the price been increased?

ARITHMETIC

The ratio in which price has been increased

$$= \frac{\text{New Price}}{\text{Old Price}} = \frac{\text{6s. } 0\frac{1}{2}\text{d.}}{\text{4s. } 7\frac{1}{2}\text{d.}}$$

$$= \frac{145 \text{ halfpence}}{111 \text{ halfpence}} = \frac{\mathbf{145}}{\mathbf{111}}.$$

In a case of this kind where the ratio is of two fairly large numbers a better comparison is made by expressing the result in the form $x:1$, i.e. make the denominator 1, by dividing by it.

$\therefore$ Ratio,
New Price: Old Price = 1·31:1.

$$\begin{array}{r} 111)\overline{145}(1\cdot31 \\ \underline{111} \\ 340 \\ \underline{333} \\ 70 \end{array}$$

Ex. 3. A photograph 12 cm. by 9 cm. is to be enlarged to fit a frame of longer side 16 cm. What length is the shorter side of the frame? What is the ratio of the new area of the picture to the original area, if the shape is unchanged?

$$\frac{\text{Shorter side of frame}}{\text{Longer side of frame}} = \frac{\text{Shorter side of photograph}}{\text{Longer side of photograph}}$$

$$\therefore \frac{\text{Shorter side}}{16} = \frac{9}{12}$$

i.e. Shorter side $= \frac{9}{12} \times 16 = \mathbf{12 \text{ cm.}}$

$$\frac{\text{New area}}{\text{Old area}} = \frac{16 \times 12}{12 \times 9} = \frac{16}{9}$$

$\therefore$ **Ratio of the new area to the original area is 16:9.**

EXERCISE 1

1. Find the ratio of 165 yd. to 1 mi.
2. What is the ratio of 8s. 6d. to 5s. 8d.?
3. It costs £1 15s. a day to stay in a hotel in September, and 14 gns. a week in August. By comparing the cost of a week's holiday in September with that of a week's holiday in August find the ratio of the costs, in lowest terms.

4. Baker earns £2 12s. 6d. a day in a five-day week, and Hughes earns £14 a week. Find the ratio of their earnings. (Compare the amount earned in either one day *or* one week by both.)

5. During a strike two-fifths of Smith's wages were lost. In what ratio was his income reduced?

6. During the week of a furniture sale, all furniture was reduced in the same ratio. If a piano originally costing £175 was offered at £120, what would be the sale price of a coffee table originally costing £7?

7. A man pays 8s. 6d. tax in every £1 he gets. What is the ratio of his net income (after paying tax) to the tax he pays?

8. John has a bar of chocolate and he gives two-fifths of it to his younger sister. What is the ratio of the amount he now has to the amount given away?

9. Express £1 7s. 6d. as an exact decimal of £6 13s. 4d.

10. The ratio of a quantity A is to B as 4:5, and B is to C as 2:3. Find C if A is 32.

11. The profits of a firm totalled £3618 in 1957. If these profits are to be divided among three partners in the ratio 4:3:2, find how much each receives.

12. A company manufactured cosmetics which it marketed at twice the cost of production in 1956. During 1957 the cost increased in the ratio of 4:3 whilst the selling price was increased only in the ratio of 5:4. Calculate the ratio of the 1957 profit to the 1956 profit on each article.

2. Variation and Proportion

(a) **Direct Variation.** When two quantities are so related that their ratio remains constant, then either is said to *vary directly* as the other. If one quantity is y and the other is x, the ratio $\dfrac{y}{x} = k$ (a constant), i.e. $y = kx$, so if $x = 1$, $y = k$; $x = 2$, $y = 2k$ and so on.

As an illustration, consider speed (in m.p.h.). It is defined as the rate of change of distance, or

$$\text{Speed (m.p.h.)} = \frac{\text{Distance (miles)}}{\text{Time (hours)}}$$

If the speed is v m.p.h., distance s miles and time t hours, we have

$$v = \frac{s}{t}$$

∴ $s = vt$ on multiplying both sides by t.

Suppose a car is travelling at 30 m.p.h.

then $s = 30t$.

In 10 minutes the car travels $30 \times \frac{10}{60} = 5$ miles

20	,,	,, ,,	,,	$30 \times \frac{20}{60} = 10$	,,
30	,,	,, ,,	,,	$30 \times \frac{30}{60} = 15$	,, etc.

If we draw a graph[1] with minutes plotted on the horizontal axis and miles on the vertical axis, we find that the points obtained by marking off 10 minutes horizontally and 5 miles vertically (i.e. the point A whose *coordinates* are (10, 5)); 20 minutes horizontally and 10 miles vertically (i.e. the point B whose coordinates are (20, 10)); and so on, we get a series of points A, B, C . . . lying on a straight line passing through the origin O.

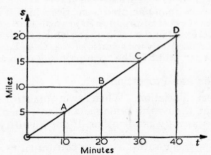

(*b*) **Inverse Variation.** Definition. The *reciprocal* of a number x is one divided by x, i.e. $\frac{1}{x}$.

When two quantities are so related that one of them

[1] Graphs are explained in Chapter 10.

varies directly as the *reciprocal* of the other, the numbers are said to *vary inversely*. If one quantity is y and the other is x, then y varies as $\frac{1}{x}$, i.e. $y = k \times \frac{1}{x}$ (where k is a constant), or more briefly

$$\mathbf{y = \frac{k}{x}}$$

If $x = 1$, $y = k$; if $x = 2$, $y = \frac{1}{2}k$; if $x = 3$, $y = \frac{1}{3}k$ an l so on.

Again consider the equation

$$\text{Speed (m.p.h.)} = \frac{\text{Distance (miles)}}{\text{Time (hours)}}$$

Using the same notation as before

$$v = \frac{s}{t}$$

Suppose a car has to travel a definite distance, say 120 miles, then

$$v = \frac{120}{t}.$$

If the time taken were 2 hr., $v = \frac{120}{2} = 60$ m.p.h.

,, ,, ,, ,, ,, 3 ,, $v = \frac{120}{3} = 40$,,

,, ,, ,, ,, ,, 4 ,, $v = \frac{120}{4} = 30$,,

,, ,, ,, ,, ,, 5 ,, $v = \frac{120}{5} = 24$,, etc.

If we were to draw a graph of speed against time, i.e. time (say in hours) horizontally and speed (in m.p.h.) vertically we would no longer have a straight line, as we see by plotting the points (2, 60), (3, 40), (4, 30), etc.

(The curve we get is actually called a rectangular hyperbola.) (*See overleaf.*)

Had we, however, plotted a graph of $\frac{1}{v}$ against t we *would* have obtained a straight-line graph. We could have forecast this, because, taking our present example,

$$v = \frac{120}{t}$$

$$\therefore vt = 120$$

$$\text{i.e. } t = \frac{120}{v} = 120 \times \frac{1}{v}.$$

Putting $\frac{1}{v} = w$, then $t = 120w$, which is an equation of direct variation connecting t and w, and as we saw in

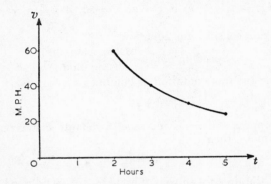

paragraph 2(*a*) above, this will yield a straight-line graph.

Ex. 4. Jones drives $38\frac{1}{2}$ miles in 1 hr. 3 min. How long would it take him to drive 44 miles at the same speed?

(This is an example of direct variation: the greater the distance the greater the time.)

If the distance is increased in the ratio $44:38\frac{1}{2}$, then the time is increased in the same ratio; but the time was originally 63 min.

$$\therefore \text{New time} = 63 \times \frac{44}{38\frac{1}{2}}$$

$$= \frac{63 \times 88}{77} = \textbf{72 min.}$$

Ex. 5. If 6 men take 20 days to paint a row of houses, how long would 8 men take?

(This is an example of inverse variation: the greater the number of men the shorter the time taken.)

If the number of men is *increased* in the ratio 8:6, the number of days is *decreased* in the ratio 6:8, i.e. it is multiplied by $\frac{6}{8}$.

$$\therefore \text{ Number of days} = 20 \times \tfrac{6}{8}$$
$$= \mathbf{15.}$$

When the problem takes a more elaborate form, it is often useful to invent compound units. If 5 men are employed for 6 days they will have done 30 man-days of work.

Ex. 6. It costs £46 to hire 3 lorries for 5 days. How much could it cost to hire 7 lorries for 8 days?

Cost of hiring 3 lorries for 5 days is 15 lorry-days

   ,,   ,,   ,,   7   ,,   ,, 8 ,,   ,, 56   ,,

$\therefore$ Cost has increased in the ratio 56:15

$$\therefore \text{ New cost} = £46 \times \tfrac{56}{15}$$
$$= £3 \text{ 1s. 4d.} \times 56$$
$$= \mathbf{£171\ 14s.\ 8d.}$$

EXERCISE 2

1. The cost of a holiday is 19 gns. a week. How much would it cost, in £ s. d., for 12 days?

2. If the average speed of a train is increased from 45 m.p.h. to 50 m.p.h. for a journey of 120 miles, find how much time is saved?

3. Three partners would have to provide £3200 each to buy a business. What would be the cost to be borne by each, if there were 5 partners?

4. An expedition is equipped with provisions for 28 days. How long would the food last if each member had his ration reduced by a quarter?

5. If 3 men are paid £25 1s. 0d. for 4 days' building construction, how much would it cost to employ 5 men for 7 days?

6. Williams & Co. have undertaken to build a road 2 miles long in 12 weeks. They employ 69 men. After 10 weeks 1½ miles have been constructed. How many more men

must now be employed to complete the work on schedule?

3. Proportional Parts

If a quantity is divided into two or more parts so that there are a units in the first part, b in the second, and so on, we say that the quantity is divided in the ratio $a:b \cdot c$, etc.

For example, if £150 is divided into three parts in the ratio 2:3:5, then the first part contains 2 shares, the second part contains 3 shares and the third part contains 5 shares. Altogether there are $2 + 3 + 5 \ (= 10)$ shares.

$\therefore$ The first part contains $\frac{2}{10}$ of the whole, i.e.

$$£150 \times \tfrac{2}{10} = £30$$

$\therefore$ The second part contains $\frac{3}{10}$ of the whole, i.e.

$$£150 \times \tfrac{3}{10} = £45$$

$\therefore$ The third part contains $\frac{5}{10}$ of the whole, i.e.

$$£150 \times \tfrac{5}{10} = £75$$

Ex. 7. A legacy is to be divided among May, John and Hilda in the ratio of 4:3:2. If the legacy is £720, find how much each receives.

Altogether there are $4 + 3 + 2$ shares, i.e. 9 shares.

$\therefore$ May receives $£\frac{4}{9} \times 720 =$ **£320**

John receives $£\frac{3}{9} \times 720 =$ **£240**

Hilda receives $£\frac{2}{9} \times 720 =$ **£160**

(Notice that $\frac{4}{9} + \frac{3}{9} + \frac{2}{9} = 1$, i.e. one whole legacy.)

EXERCISE 3

1. Divide £50 among 4 people in the ratio 6:5:3:1.
2. Three men and 2 women are employed. The earnings of a man is to that of a woman as 4:3. If the total amount earned is £450, find how much each receives. (There are 3 men each with 4 shares, and 2 women each with 3 shares.)
3. Three farmers, Jones, Wright and Siddons share grazing land for their cattle. Jones and Wright each have 75 head of cattle and Siddons has 90. Jones removes his

cattle after 2 months but both Wright and Siddons graze theirs for 3 months. If the total rent is £32 5s., calculate how much each should pay.

4. Find which town has the greater proportional rate of increase of population: Town A (1956)—217,800, (1957)—222,300; Town B (1956)—70,500, (1957)—71,900.

5. A tap can fill a bath with water in 5 minutes. The bath is emptied in 7 minutes when the plug is removed. How long would it take to fill the bath when the tap is on and the plug is removed?

6. What is the ratio of 4¼ to 2¼? Find the cost of 4¼ tons of coal if 2¼ tons cost £22 0s. 3d.

4. Averages

When an experiment is repeated a number of times, it is of value to know the average result. For example, a shopkeeper may make profits of £30, £28, £37, £33, £36, £24, £29, £35 in 8 successive weeks. In order to assess his average income during that time it is only necessary to add these profits and to divide the result by the number of items added.

$$\therefore \text{ Average income} = \tfrac{1}{8} \{30 + 28 + 37 + 33 + 36 + 24 + 29 + 35\}$$
$$= \tfrac{1}{8} \times 252 = \textbf{£31 10s.}$$

That the average gives the *best* estimate of a number of events of this type is shown in books on statistics.

Sometimes an item may be repeated a number of times. The principle remains unchanged.

Ex. 8. 7 lb. of tea at 7s. 6d. a lb. are blended with 3 lb. of tea at 8s. 4d. a lb. At what price should the mixture be valued?

There are 10 lb. altogether.

$$\therefore \text{ Average price} = \tfrac{1}{10} \{7 \times 7\text{s. } 6\text{d.} + 3 \times 8\text{s. } 4\text{d.}\}$$
$$= \tfrac{1}{10} \{52\text{s. } 6\text{d.} + 25\text{s.}\}$$
$$= \frac{77\text{s. } 6\text{d.}}{10} = \textbf{7s. 9d.}$$

When the average of a set of measurements, which differ only by fairly small amounts from one another, is required the following artifice will often save labour.

Ex. 9. The heights of 12 boys who are 15 years of age are 5 ft. $11\frac{1}{2}$ in., 5 ft. $8\frac{1}{2}$ in., 5 ft. $8\frac{1}{2}$ in., 6 ft. 0 in., 5 ft. $5\frac{1}{2}$ in., 5 ft. 4 in., 5 ft. $9\frac{1}{2}$ in., 6 ft. $1\frac{1}{2}$ in., 6 ft. $2\frac{1}{2}$ in., 5 ft. 10 in., 5 ft. 11 in., 5 ft. $8\frac{1}{2}$ in.

Let us consider the difference between these heights and an *assumed* average of 6 ft. 0 in. We get the following differences:

Difference between actual height and 6 ft., in inches	
−	+
$0\frac{1}{2}$	0
$3\frac{1}{2}$	$1\frac{1}{2}$
$3\frac{1}{2}$	$2\frac{1}{2}$
$6\frac{1}{2}$	
8	
$2\frac{1}{2}$	
2	
1	/
$3\frac{1}{2}$	
31	4

∴ Total difference $= -31 + 4$
$= -27$ in.
Divide by 12 (the number of boys).
∴ Average difference $= -\frac{27}{12} = -2\frac{1}{4}$ in.
∴ Average height of each boy
$= 6$ ft. 0 in. $- 2\frac{1}{4}$ in.
$= $ **5 ft. $9\frac{3}{4}$ in.**

A curious anomaly can arise in calculating averages at cricket. It is the convention that when a batsman is "not out" at the end of an innings, he is credited with any runs made, but is not counted as having had an innings. Consider the following example.

Brown scored in 8 successive innings 5, 4, 6, 2 not out, 4 not out, 3, 5 not out, 4.

Number of runs scored $= 5 + 4 + 6 + 2 +$
$$4 + 3 + 5 + 4$$
$$= 33$$

Number of completed innings $= 5$

$\therefore$ Average $= \frac{33}{5} =$ **6·6.**

His average is therefore more than the number of runs he actually made in any innings! The fault lies in the system adopted; that an incomplete innings should not be counted is a purely arbitrary rule, and is not based on mathematical principles. The result can hardly be expected to bear close analytical scrutiny.

EXERCISE 4

1. Find the average of £624, £561, £733, £247, £995.

2. Find the average price of 18 cwt. of coal at 9s. 6d. a cwt. and 22 cwt. at 10s. 3d. a cwt.

3. Express 125:483 in the ratio of 1:N.

4. If it takes 42 minutes to cover a journey at 25 m.p.h., how long would it take at 35 m.p.h.?

5. The weights of a class of 15 boys were found to be as follows: 7 st. 10 lb., 8 st. 11 lb., 6 st. 1 lb., 7 st. 9 lb., 7 st. 3 lb., 6 st. 10 lb., 8 st. 0 lb., 8 st. 5 lb., 7 st. 6 lb., 5 st. 13 lb., 6 st. 6 lb., 7 st. 4 lb., 7 st. 7 lb., 8 st. 1 lb., 6 st. 9 lb. Find the average weight of a boy.

6. A train travels 30 miles at an average speed of 40 m.p.h., and a further 25 miles at an average speed of 45 m.p.h. Find the average speed for the whole journey of 55 miles.

7. Smith's batting average for 8 completed innings is 16·5. He bats for a ninth innings, also completed, and his new average for all 9 innings is found to be 18. How many did he score in his ninth innings?

CHAPTER NINE

PERCENTAGE, PROFIT AND LOSS

1. Percentage

When we wish to compare quantities, fractions are not always helpful. Nor are decimals necessarily suitable for quick calculation. For example, suppose we wish to compare the following:

   (a) A profit of 3s. on a cost price of £1
   (b) A profit of 2s. 6d. on a cost price of 15s.
   (b) A profit of 2s. on a cost price of 12s. 6d.

We need the fractions $\dfrac{3}{20}$; $\dfrac{2\frac{1}{2}}{15} = \dfrac{5}{30} = \dfrac{1}{6}$, $\dfrac{2}{12\frac{1}{2}} = \dfrac{4}{25}$.

We could bring them to the same denominator, or express each as decimals. Neither is convenient for some purposes. In such cases we arrange matters so that all fractions considered have a denominator of 100.

Now (a) $\dfrac{3}{20} = \dfrac{3}{20} \times \dfrac{100}{100}$

$$= \dfrac{3}{\underset{1}{20}} \times \overset{5}{100} \text{ per 100}$$

$= 15\%$ (we write the denominator 100 as the symbol %, called "per cent." from the Latin, per centum = out of 100).

i.e. $\dfrac{3}{20}$ is the same as 15 (parts) out of 100 (parts).

Similarly (b) $\dfrac{1}{6} = \dfrac{1}{6} \times 100\%$
$$= \dfrac{100}{6}\% = 16\tfrac{2}{3}\%$$
(c) $\dfrac{4}{25} = \dfrac{4}{25} \times 100\%$
$$= 16\%$$

∴ The best profit in the above three transactions is (b), relative to the others. It is the best return on outlay. It is not necessarily the largest cash profit; (a) is the largest.

We say that a profit of 3s. on an outlay of £1 represents a 15% profit (fifteen per cent. profit).

The symbols C.P. for cost price, and S.P. for selling price will be used frequently. The difference between them is the profit made.

$$\text{i.e. S.P.} - \text{C.P.} = \text{Profit.}$$

Ex. 1. Smith obtains 17 marks out of a possible 40 in a test. What percentage is this?

$$\frac{17}{40} = \frac{17}{40} \times 100\% = 42\tfrac{1}{2}\%.$$

Ex. 2. Express $17\tfrac{1}{2}\%$ as: (a) a fraction in lowest terms; (b) a decimal.

$$(a)\ \ 17\tfrac{1}{2}\% = \frac{17\tfrac{1}{2}}{100} = \frac{35}{200} = \frac{7}{40}.$$

$$(b)\ \ \tfrac{7}{40} = 0{\cdot}175$$

$$\frac{4\overline{)0{\cdot}700}}{0{\cdot}175}$$

The following percentages of £1 are very useful to remember

5% of £1 $= \frac{5}{100} \times$ £1 $= \frac{1}{20} \times$ 20s. $=$ **1s.**

$\therefore$ **5% of £1 is a shilling in the pound**

  10% of £1 is two shillings in the pound

  $2\tfrac{1}{2}\%$ of £1 is sixpence in the pound.

Ex. 3. Find the value of 6% of £3 12s. 6d.

There are several possible methods. One or other of the following is recommended.

Method 1. (Practice)

	£	s.	d.
100% is	3	12	6
10% is		7	3	($\div$ 10)
5% is		3	7·50 ($\div$ 2)
1% is			8·70 ($\div$ 5)
		4	4·20

$\therefore$ **Required value is 4s. 4d. to nearest 1d.**

Method 2. (Decimals)

6% of £3 12s. 6d. = 0·06 × £3·625

$= £0·2175$

$= \textbf{4s. 4d.}$

$$\begin{array}{r} 3625 \\ \underline{6 \times} \\ £\mathbf{0}·21750 \\ \overline{\text{s.}\overline{4}·350} \quad (\times\ 20) \\ \text{d.}\overline{4}·2 \quad (\times\ 12) \end{array}$$

EXERCISE 1

1. Express the following as percentages:

(a) $\frac{1}{5}$ (b) $\frac{1}{4}$ (c) $\frac{2}{3}$ (d) $\frac{7}{11}$ (e) $1\frac{1}{8}$ (f) $\frac{3}{700}$.

2. Express the following as fractions in lowest terms:

(a) 15% (b) 28% (c) $27\frac{1}{2}$% (d) 160% (e) $33\frac{1}{3}$% (f) 0·4%.

3. Express the following as decimals, correct to 4 decimal places, where not exact:

(a) 35% (b) $33\frac{1}{3}$% (c) $107\frac{1}{2}$% (d) $3\frac{3}{4}$% (e) $1\frac{7}{11}$% (f) $3\frac{3}{7}$%.

4. Express (a) 14 as a percentage of 45

(b) 2s. 6d. as a percentage of £1

(c) 3s. 6d. as a percentage of 25s.

(d) 1 lb. 6 oz. as a percentage of 2 lb. 1 oz.

(e) $7\frac{1}{2}$d. as a percentage of 5s.

5. Find the value of:

(a) $7\frac{1}{2}$% of £120

(b) $2\frac{1}{4}$% of £85

(c) 16% of 3 gall. 1 qt.

(d) 4% of £7 11s. 6d.

(e) $3\frac{1}{2}$% of £74 16s. 2d.

It is worth memorising the following relationships.

100% = 1 = 1	5% = $\frac{1}{20}$ = 0·05
50% = $\frac{1}{2}$ = 0·5	$33\frac{1}{3}$% = $\frac{1}{3}$ = 0·33...
25% = $\frac{1}{4}$ = 0·25	$66\frac{2}{3}$% = $\frac{2}{3}$ = 0·66...
10% = $\frac{1}{10}$ = 0·1	75% = $\frac{3}{4}$ = 0·75

2. Percentage Profit

Suppose an electric iron were bought for £2 and sold at a profit of 25%.

The profit = 25% of Cost Price

$$= \tfrac{25}{100} \times \text{C.P.}$$

$$= \pounds 2 \times \tfrac{25}{100} \text{ (for C.P.} = \pounds 2)$$

$$= \pounds \tfrac{1}{2} = \textbf{10s.}$$

Also the S.P. = C.P. + profit = $\pounds 2$ + 10s. = **£2 10s.**
We see at once that this is a particular case of the formula:

$$\textbf{Profit} = \frac{\textbf{Percentage Profit}}{\textbf{100}} \times \textbf{C.P.} \qquad (1)$$

In another form, this gives on rearrangement:

Percentage Profit $\times$ C.P. = 100 $\times$ Profit

i.e. **Percentage Profit** = $\textbf{100} \times \dfrac{\textbf{Profit}}{\textbf{C.P.}}$ (2)

Ex. 4. An article is bought for $\pounds 3$ and sold for $\pounds 3$ 17s. 6d.
What is the percentage profit?

C.P. = $\pounds 3$, S.P. = $\pounds 3$ 17s. 6d. $\therefore$ Profit = 17s. 6d.

$$\therefore \text{ Percentage profit} = \frac{17\text{s. }6\text{d.}}{\pounds 3} \times 100\%$$

$$= \frac{17\tfrac{1}{2}\text{s.}}{60\text{s.}} \times 100$$

$$= \frac{35}{120} \times 100$$

$$= 29\tfrac{1}{6}\%.$$

Now it is often important to compare cost price and
selling price of goods. Suppose that in a certain transaction a profit of $p\%$ is made (i.e. percentage profit is p).
The *profit* is always worked on the *cost price*, *not* on the
selling price.

If, then, the cost price had been 100, the selling price
would have been 100 + p. (For $p\%$ profit means p
pounds profit for every 100 pounds outlay.)

Now formula (1) above states that

$$\text{Profit} = \frac{\text{Percentage Profit}}{100} \times \text{C.P.}$$

but Profit = S.P. − C.P., and Percentage Profit is p.

$$\therefore \text{S.P.} - \text{C.P.} = \frac{p}{100} \times \text{C.P.}$$

$$\therefore 100 \times \text{S.P.} - 100 \times \text{C.P.} = p \times \text{C.P.}$$
So $100 \times \text{S.P.} = (100 + p) \times \text{C.P.}$

$$\therefore \textbf{S.P.} = \frac{100 + p}{100} \times \textbf{C.P.} \qquad . \qquad . \quad (3)$$

$$\text{or } \textbf{C.P.} = \frac{100}{100 + p} \times \textbf{S.P.} \qquad . \qquad . \quad (4)$$

These formulae are very useful and are easily under-stood and remembered if the work is laid out as under.

Ex. 5. A watch is sold for £3 12s. at a profit of 8%. How much did it cost originally?

If the C.P. had been 100, the S.P. would have been 108. Let the actual C.P. be x; the actual S.P. is 72s.

C.P.	S.P.
x	72s.
100	108

By direct comparison

$$\frac{x}{100} = \frac{72}{108} \text{ s.}$$

$$\therefore x = \frac{100 \times 72}{108} \text{ s. (as in formula (4) above)}$$

$$= \frac{100 \times 72}{108}\text{s.} = \frac{200}{3}\text{s.}$$

$$= 66\tfrac{2}{3}\text{s.} = \textbf{£3 6s. 8d.}$$

Ex. 6. As a result of evacuation during hostilities the population of a town decreased to 79,200, representing a drop of 12%. What was the previous population?

F.P.	S.P.
x 100	79200 88

F.P. = First Population
S.P. = Second Population

As before, let F.P. $= x$

$$\therefore \frac{x}{100} = \frac{79200}{88}$$

$$\therefore \quad x = \frac{100 \times \overset{\overset{900}{\cancel{7200}}}{\cancel{79200}}}{\underset{\underset{1}{8}}{88}}$$

$$= \mathbf{90,000.}$$

Ex. 7. A toy costing 8s. 4d. is sold at a profit of 20%. What is the selling price?

C.P.	S.P.
8s. 4d. 100	x 120

Here the S.P. ($= x$, say) is the unknown quantity.

$$\therefore \frac{x}{120} = \frac{8s.\ 4d.}{100}$$

$$\therefore \quad x = \frac{120 \times 100d.}{100}$$

$$= 120d. = \mathbf{10s.}$$

Ex. 8. An author receives £28 on account for a set of articles. If this represents 35% of the amount due altogether, how much more can he expect to receive?

£28 is 35% of the total, so that 65% has still to be paid (to make the total of 100%).

Let £x be the remainder due.

Amount Paid	Amount Due
28	x
35	65

$$\therefore \frac{x}{65} = \frac{28}{35}$$

$$\therefore x = \frac{\overset{4}{28} \times \overset{13}{65}}{\underset{\underset{1}{5}}{35}} = 52.$$

∴ There is £52 more payment due later.

EXERCISE 2

1. Find the selling price if:
    (a) cost price is £4, profit 20%
    (b) cost price is £3 15s., profit 15%
    (c) cost price is 12s. 6d., loss 20%.

2. Find the percentage profit or loss if:
    (a) cost price is £4, selling price is £4 10s.
    (b) cost price is £4, selling price is £3
    (c) cost price is £2 1s., selling price is £2 14s. 8d.

3. Find the cost price if an article is sold for:
    (a) £3 at a profit of 20%
    (b) £3 4s. at a loss of 20%
    (c) £1 7s. 4d. at a profit of $33\frac{1}{3}$%.

4. Find the value of the following, correct to the nearest 1d.:
    (a) $2\frac{1}{2}$% of £7 17s. 8d.
    (b) $5\frac{1}{2}$% of £3 11s. 7d.
    (c) 7% of £5 18s. 2d.

5. The diameter of the earth is 7,913 miles and that of the sun is 864,367 miles. What percentage of the sun's diameter is that of the earth? (Correct to 2 significant figures.)

6. During a year Smith spends £1026, which represents 95% of his income. How much does he save?

7. The rate in the pound charged in Chislehurst and Sidcup in 1956 was 16s. 8d. Of this, household refuse removal cost 7·15d. What percentage of the rate in the pound is this?

8. To insure a building under a comprehensive policy the premium asked by many large companies is 2s. 3d. per £100 insured. What percentage is this of the sum insured? What would it cost to insure a house worth £4250?

3. Harder Percentage Problems

There are extensions of the principles indicated above which have practical applications in everyday life.

We shall first consider the changes which take place in successive transactions. Goods are sold by a manufacturer to a retailer, who in turn sells them to a customer. There is a profit made on each part of the business, but in dealing with the percentage change in price *we may not add the successive percentages together*. They lead to *multiplication* as will be seen from the following example.

Ex. 9. Smith & Co. make chairs at a cost of £3 10s. They sell them to Brown & Tomkins' Furniture Stores at a profit of 20%. The price at which they are sold to a customer ensures a profit of 25% for Brown & Tomkins. What is the retail price and how much per cent. is this greater than the original cost price?

C.P. Manufacturer's cost

S.P.1 Wholesale selling price

S.P.2 Retail selling price

C.P.	S.P.1	S.P.2
£3. 10s.		
100	120	
	100	125

We see at once that

$$\frac{\text{S.P.2}}{\text{S.P.1}} = \tfrac{125}{100}, \text{ i.e. S.P.2} = \tfrac{125}{100} \times \text{S.P.1}$$

Also $\dfrac{\text{S.P.1}}{\text{C.P.}} = \tfrac{120}{100}, \text{ i.e. S.P.1} = \tfrac{120}{100} \times \text{C.P.}$

$$\begin{aligned}
\therefore \text{S.P.2} &= \tfrac{125}{100} \times \tfrac{120}{100} \times \text{C.P.} \\
&= \tfrac{125}{100} \times \tfrac{120}{100} \times 70\text{s.} \\
&= 105\text{s.} = \text{£5 5s.}
\end{aligned}$$

Also $\dfrac{\text{S.P.2}}{\text{C.P.}} = \tfrac{125}{100} \times \tfrac{120}{100} = \tfrac{3}{2}.$

$\therefore$ If C.P. is 100, S.P.2 is $\tfrac{3}{2} \times 100 = 150.$

$\therefore$ Percentage increase is **50%**. (Not 45% as would have been obtained by adding the successive increases per cent. We could, if we had known them, have added the *actual* profits, and found the percentage increase altogether as

$$\frac{\text{1st Profit} + \text{2nd Profit}}{\text{Cost Price}} \times 100.)$$

Let us next investigate the percentage error made in measuring lengths, areas and volumes. Now error is the difference between calculated and true values, so percentage error is given by

Percentage error

$$= \frac{\text{Calculated value} \sim \text{True value}}{\text{True value}} \times 100 \quad . \quad (\text{1})$$

The symbol $\sim$ means difference between the quantities on either side of it, putting the larger one first. It is not difficult to see that in practice the true value may not be known exactly, although the greatest margin of error may be. In this case a practical modification of (1) would be

Percentage error *is less than*

$$\frac{\text{Maximum Error}}{\text{Calculated Value}} \times 100 \quad . \quad . \quad (\text{2})$$

The relationship (2), which is not an equation, can lead to some fairly difficult problems, so we shall content ourselves with applications of equation (1) and very simple cases of (2). It is instructive to think for a moment of an application of (2), however, as in measurement with a ruler. A ruler is not an *exact* instrument. Suppose we find that the length of a line is 8 in. We can assume that the ruler is accurate within $\frac{1}{10}$ of an inch. Therefore, the percentage error in taking the length of the line as a true 8 in. is likely to be less than

$$\frac{0\cdot1}{8} \times 100\%, \text{ i.e. } 1\tfrac{1}{4}\%.$$

We cannot measure 8 in. exactly, however hard we try, so we cannot find the exact percentage error.

Ex. 10. A rectangular field 40 yd. long and 120 yd. wide is called by Farmer Brown a one-acre field. What is the percentage error?

Actual area = 40 × 120 = 4800 sq. yd.
Rough area = 1 acre = 4840 sq. yd.

$$\therefore \text{ Percentage error} = \frac{4840 - 4800}{4800} \times 100$$

$$= \frac{40 \times 100}{4800} = \frac{5}{6}\%$$

(i.e. it is less than 1%).

Discount. Discount is a reduction given on the normal price. A shopkeeper may offer a reduction in the marked price of goods during a sale. A typical example would read "During this week there is a reduction of 10% on all marked prices". It could equally well read "10% discount on all marked prices during this week".

Now 10% of £1 = 2s.; and the sale price is 100 − 10 = 90 per cent. of the marked price, i.e. 18s. has to be paid out of each £1 marked.

Alternatively, we have Sale Price = $\frac{90}{100}$ × Retail Price.

Ex. 11. A tape recorder is sold for 58 gns. normally, but a discount of 5% is allowed for immediate cash payment. How much would a customer pay if he offered outright purchase?

Normal charge = 58 gns. = £60 18s.

Reduction of 5% means that reduced charge is $\frac{95}{100}$ of normal charge.

$\therefore$ Cash payment = £$60\frac{9}{10} \times \frac{95}{100}$

= **£57 17s. 1d.**

correct to the nearest 1d.

$$
\begin{array}{r}
60.9 \\
0.95 \times \\
\hline
3.045 \\
54.81 \\
\hline
57.855 \\
\hline
17.10 \\
\hline
1.2
\end{array}
$$

EXERCISE 3

1. During each year a car loses 15% of its value at the beginning of the year. What is its value in January 1959, if it cost £800 in January 1956?

2. Smith has £1000 worth of goods. He sells £850 worth at 10% profit and the remainder at 5% loss. What percentage profit did he make on the whole transaction?

3. A shopkeeper sells a clock for £3, thereby making a profit of 20%. During a sale he allows a discount of 10% on the marked price. What is his new percentage profit?

4. A merchant pays £1 7s. 6d. for a pair of steps. He normally sells them at a profit of 20%, but allows a discount of 1s. in the pound during a January sale. What is the sale price (to the nearest penny)?

5. A room is measured roughly as 10 ft. 6 in. by 12 ft. 6 in. Its true area is 120 sq. ft. What is the percentage error in measurement of the area?

6. A grocer buys sugar at £3 14s. for a one-hundredweight chest. He sells it at 10d. a pound, but 5% is wasted in making it up into bags. What is (a) his percentage profit, (b) his actual profit on one chest?

7. What percentage increase is necessary to change a loss of 5% into a profit of 5%?

8. A householder spends one-sixth of his income on rent, one-quarter on food and one-ninth on clothes. He spends £520 on these items in 1955. During 1956 his rent increases by 5%, his food costs by 10%, and the cost of clothes by 8%. How much does he spend on these in 1956? What is the overall percentage increase on rent, food and clothes?

4. Mixtures

An introduction to problems involving mixtures was given in the previous chapter, under the section on averages. We will now consider inverse problems on mixtures, and include percentage profit.

Ex. 12. In what proportion should coffee at 6s. a lb. be blended with coffee at 7s. 4d. a lb. if the mixture is to be sold at 7s. 11d. a lb., thereby making a profit of 25%?

We have $\dfrac{\text{C.P. of mixture}}{\text{S.P.}} = \dfrac{100}{125} = \dfrac{4}{5}$

∴ C.P. of mixture $= \dfrac{4}{5} \times$ 7s. 11d. $= \dfrac{4}{5} \times$ 95d.
$= $ 76d. $= $ 6s. 4d.

Coffee at 6s. a lb. costs 4d. a lb. *less* than mixture.
Coffee at 7s. 4d. a lb. costs 12d. a lb. *more* than mixture.
∴ **3 parts of the cheaper coffee are mixed with 1 part of dearer.**

[For in each 4 lb., 3 × 4d. (= 12d.) too little is charged and 1 × 12d. (= 12d.) too much is charged.]

Alternatively, the second part of the calculation can be done very neatly as follows:

MIXTURE

Cheaper tea 6s.   12 parts of cheaper tea

6s. 4d.

Dearer tea 7s. 4d.   4 parts of dearer tea

i.e. number of parts of cheaper tea to number of parts of dearer tea is 12:4, i.e. 3:1.

EXERCISE 4

1. Coffee at 7s. 3d. a lb. is blended with coffee at 6s. 5d. a lb. In what proportion should they be mixed, if the resultant blend is worth 6s. 8½d. a lb.?

2. 21 lb. of tea at 6s. 8d. a lb. are blended with 36 lb. of tea at 7s. 6d. a lb. At what price per lb. must the mixture be sold to make a profit of 14%?

3. Find the percentage profit on selling, at 7 lb. for 8s. 4d., a commodity which cost £4 13s. 4d. a cwt.

4. If milk costing 4s. a gallon is mixed with water in the ratio of 5:1 and the mixture is sold at 6¾d. a pint, what percentage profit is made? (Neglect the cost of the water.)

5. Wine at 17s. 6d. a bottle is mixed with wine at 23s. a bottle. In what proportion are they mixed, if the mixture is sold for 24s. 2d. a bottle, giving a profit of 25%?

6. In a club of 80 members, 62 play bridge, 74 attend the club dances and 55 play tennis on the club courts. What is the *least* possible number of members who take part in all three activities?

7. Fifty-three passengers are riding in a bus. Some take 3d. tickets and the rest have 4d. tickets. Altogether their fares come to 14s. 6d. How many took 3d. tickets?

CHAPTER TEN

ARITHMETICAL GRAPHS

1. Plotting and Interpreting Graphs

Information provided in words often takes some time to assimilate. If, however, we can represent the situation pictorially we can grasp quickly the salient features present. Reading a set of numbers gives no clear image to remember, whereas a diagram will be retained in mind for a considerable time.

It is accepted practice nowadays to give diagrams and pictures wherever possible to clarify important points in many forms of study, particularly if it is scientific or technical. For example, only a limited number of people would read a book on animal life, and having read it still less would not have forgotten most of the contents within a very short space of time. On the other hand, how vast a number is enthralled by natural-history films! It requires no great mental effort to sit back in a cinema, watching a film: reading is a sterner test of self-discipline. Visual aids form an integral part of modern education and graphs are a form of visual aid.

We will assume that we are given two quantities x and y, where y changes in value when x changes. If we wish to mark a point on a diagram to represent a *particular* pair of values of x and y, we can do so by measuring the distance of the point from each of two perpendicular straight lines, called the *axes*. We measure x horizontally (in the direction OX in fig. 1) and y vertically (in the direction OY in fig. 1). The point O where the axes meet is called the *origin*. The lines OX, OY are the horizontal and vertical axes respectively.

Suppose a cyclist is travelling at 10 m.p.h. He will go 10 miles in 1 hour, 20 miles in 2 hours and so on. We plot a series of points, laying off time (in hours) horizontally, and distance (in miles) vertically. Our first point P is found by measuring 1 hour horizontally and then laying off 10 miles vertically. We call the point P (1, 10); the numbers 1 and 10 are the *coordinates* of the point. Q is the point (2, 20) and is given by 2 hours horizontally and 20 miles vertically. Similarly we get R (3, 30) etc.

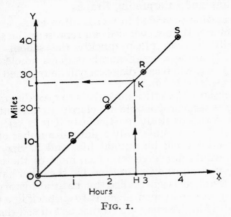

FIG. 1.

If we then join P, Q, R ... we find that we have a straight line. Further, this line passes through O, as is reasonable, for the cyclist will have gone 0 miles in 0 hours. If we wish to know how far he would go in $2\frac{3}{4}$ hours we lay off a vertical line HK, through H, the point $2\frac{3}{4}$ on OX, meeting the straight line graph at K. We then draw KL horizontally, meeting OY at L. OL $(= 27\frac{1}{2}$ miles) is the required distance.

This is a very simple example of an arithmetical graph. Graphs take various forms. Some consist of separate parallel lines (bar charts), others are polygonal (that is, they consist of connected lines joining a set of points in order. If A, B, C, D ... is the set of points in order, then the lines AB, BC, CD ... form a polygonal graph). Yet again, other graphs are smooth curves. The type of graph used depends on the nature of the information provided (see fig. 2).

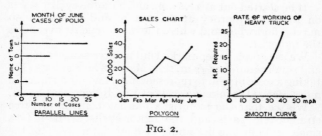

FIG. 2.

It is worth bearing in mind two points when drawing graphs:

(1) It is not essential for the origin O to be the point where both quantities being laid off shall be zero. Sometimes it is in fact undesirable for it to be zero.

(2) The scales for x and y need carefully choosing so as to make the graph as large and well shaped as possible, bearing in mind that the necessary points must all appear on the graph paper. Fig. 3 illustrates these two points.

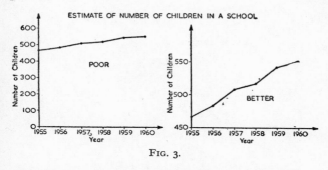

FIG. 3.

Ex. 1. A motorist travels an hour and a half at an average speed of 25 m.p.h. and then he stops for half an hour. He then continues his journey at a speed of 25 m.p.h. Find how far he has gone 2¾ hours after starting.

If he started out at 10.0 a.m. and a motor-cyclist starts on the same journey at 11.30 a.m. and travels at 50 m.p.h., find when and where the motor-cyclist overtakes the motorist.

We use graph paper marked out in large squares of 1 in. and small squares of 1/10 in. side. Mark off hours along OX, taking a scale of 1 in. to represent 1 hr. Lay off distance in miles along OY, taking a scale of 1 in. to represent 20 mi.

We see that the motorist's journey consists of three straight-line parts and the motor-cyclist's graph is a single straight line beginning 1½ hours later. We plot the points (0, 0) and (1, 25) for the motorist, stopping this line 1½ hours after starting: we then lay off a horizontal line for half an hour as he has not changed his distance: finally we lay off a line through (2, 37½) and (3, 62½), representing the last stage in his journey. The points (1½, 0), (2½, 50) will give the motor-cyclist's graph.

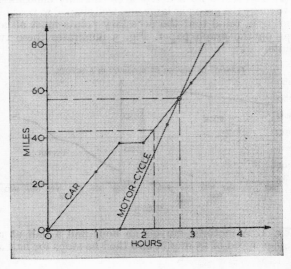

We see from the graph that (1) the motorist is $42\frac{1}{2}$ miles on his way after $2\frac{1}{4}$ hours (2) he is overtaken by the motor-cyclist at 12.45 p.m. at a distance of $56\frac{1}{4}$ miles from their starting point.

Ex. 2. A patient with a high fever has his temperature taken every four hours. From the following set of results draw a temperature graph. Find from it the highest temperature. Does the fever show signs of abating or not?

Time	Noon	4 17.11.57	8	Mid-night	4	8	Noon 18.11.57	4	8	Mid-night
Temp. °F.	100·6	101·2	101·5	102·2	102·3	101·6	101·2	101·4	102·4	102·8
Time	4	8	Noon 19.11.57	4	8	Mid-night	4	8 20.11.57	Noon	4
Temp. °F.	102·8	102·0	101·0	100·8	101·2	101·4	100·8	100·2	99·8	99·7

We lay off time horizontally using 0·3 in. for 4 hours: temperature vertically, using 1 in. for 2° F.

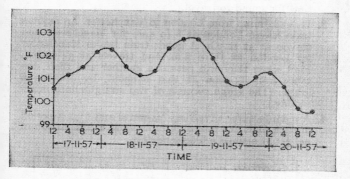

From the graph we see that the highest temperature is 102·9° F. and that it occurs at about 2 a.m. on 19th November 1957. The highest temperature on the following day was only 101·4° F. and the fall appears to be maintained. The graph suggests that the fever has passed its peak.

EXERCISE I

1. Draw a graph converting temperature in ° C. to ° F. and from it find (a) 40° C. in ° F., and (b) 60° F. in ° C

Freezing point of water	Boiling point of water
0° C.	100° C.
32° F.	212° F.

(The graph is a straight line, so the points (0, 32) and (100, 212) are sufficient.)

2. A stone is dropped down a well and the distance fallen at various times is given by the following table.

Time taken (sec.) .	0	0·5	1·0	1·5	2·0	2·5
Distance fallen (ft.) .	0	4	16	36	64	100

If the splash, when the stone strikes the water, is heard 1·8 seconds after releasing the stone, estimate the depth of the water level below ground, from a graph. If the well had been 75 ft. deep to water level, how long would it have taken before the splash was heard? (Neglecting time for sound to travel.)

3. It is 182 miles from London to Manchester. An express train leaves London at 8.40 a.m. for Manchester and travels at 52 m.p.h. A goods train leaves Manchester for London at 10.10 a.m. and travels at 34 m.p.h. Find when they will pass one another and their distance from London at that moment, by drawing a graph. (The graph consists of two straight lines intersecting.)

4. A manufacturer advertises his wares and over a period of time finds the following table gives a comparison of net profit against advertising cost.

Advertising Cost £	Profit £	Advertising Cost £	Profit £
2000	4000	7400	22000
3500	7000	9600	22000
5800	13000	11400	20800
6800	20000	14000	18000

Draw a graph of Profit (in £'s), plotted vertically, against cost of Advertising (in £'s), plotted horizontally. From your graph, find the best amount to pay in advertising.

How do you account for the shape of the graph?

2. Histograms and Frequency Distributions

Sometimes the data are of such a nature that we do not know precise points to plot. This often occurs in statistical work. In the measurement of heights of children of a particular age, it might be found that 4 were between 5 ft. 2 in. and 5 ft. 3 in., 12 were between 5 ft. 3 in. and 5 ft. 4 in. and so on. It would not be practicable to indicate every precise height, nor would it be of any real value. In such a case we plot frequency of observation against the observation range, and build up a diagram known as a histogram.

We will illustrate the principle by an example.

The following table indicates the marks obtained out of 100 by 60 candidates for an examination.

TABLE A.

Maximum 100

10	33	43	82	39	14	70	60	62	64	54	29
47	22	41	77	57	62	36	71	54	59	81	53
53	17	58	45	72	55	43	37	51	50	3	47
64	59	74	66	64	51	49	40	25	38	60	36
58	60	91	68	83	60	58	22	48	77	72	58

As it is presented (the order in which the marks appeared on the papers when examined) the information conveys nothing to the reader. It is necessary to re-organise the marks in a systematic form, and to group them into suitable classes. For example, the first class might be the number of candidates who obtained from

o to 9 marks, the second class the number who obtained
between 10 and 19 inclusive, and so on. We then have:

TABLE B.

Inclusive mark range	Frequency	Inclusive mark range	Frequency
0– 9	1	50–59	15
10–19	3	60–69	11
20–29	4	70–79	7
30–39	6	80–89	3
40–49	9	90–99	1

We now construct a histogram of frequency against
mark range.

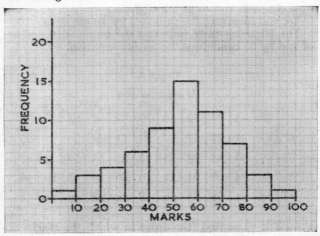

This diagram clearly indicates the distribution of
marks obtained. The marks could, however, have been
grouped under an entirely different schematic arrange-
ment.

From the previous table B construct a new table C by finding the number of candidates who obtained fewer than a specified number of marks.

TABLE C.

No. of candidates getting less *than*	Frequency	No. of candidates getting less *than*	Frequency
10	1	60	38
20	4	70	49
30	8	80	56
40	14	90	59
50	23	100	60

The table is constructed as follows:

$$1 = 1$$
$$1 + 3 = 4$$
$$1 + 3 + 4 = 8 \text{ etc.}$$

We then draw a smooth curve, called a *cumulative frequency curve* or *ogive*, with number of candidates getting fewer than x marks plotted vertically against x marks plotted horizontally.

From the ogive, various interesting results can be read off at once. The *median mark* is the mark obtained by the $\frac{60}{2} = 30$th candidate, and is 55, so half of the candidates obtained over 55%. (Strictly speaking, if there are n candidates, the median mark is that of the $\frac{n + 1}{2}$th candidate).

The *quartiles* divide the distribution into 4 equal parts. There are three quartiles, of which the middle one is the median already defined. We can alternatively calculate the median mark from the table C: 23 candidates obtained less than 50 marks, 38 obtained less than

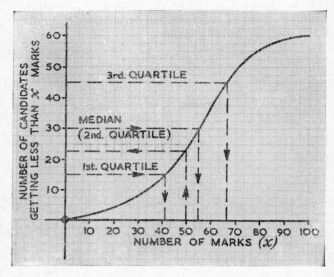

60 marks, therefore a good estimate of the mark of the 30th candidate is

$$50 + \left(\frac{30 - 23}{38 - 23}\right) \times (60 - 50) = 50 + \tfrac{7}{15} \times 10$$

$$= 54 \cdot 7 \backsimeq \mathbf{55,} \text{ which}$$

agrees with the graphical result.

Suppose the pass mark to be 50%. We see from the ogive that the number of candidates who failed is 23, so $60 - 23 = 37$ passed.

∴ The percentage of success was

$$\tfrac{37}{60} \times 100 = \mathbf{61 \cdot 7\%.}$$

EXERCISE 2

1. In a certain district it is found that the numbers of children in families gives a frequency distribution as follows:

Number of Children in the Family	0	1	2	3	4	5	6	7	8
Frequency[1]	82	147	251	107	40	9	3	1	0

Draw (a) a histogram, (b) an ogive. From the latter find the median, and indicate its position in the former.

2. Take table A (on page 103) and from it construct a frequency table like table B, but using mark ranges 0–4, 5–9, 10–14 etc., and from your table plot a histogram. Compare it with that given on page 104. Comment on their difference in appearance.

3. Construct an ogive for the following table of heights, and find the *median* height.

Height in Inches[2]	Frequency
62	1
64	4
66	12
68	22
70	17
72	9
74	5
76	1

Compare the result with the *mean* height, which is the same as the average. It is found as follows:

$$\text{Mean} = \frac{\text{Total of all the heights}}{\text{Number of heights}} = \frac{f_1 \times h_1 + f_2 \times h_2 + \dots}{f_1 + f_2 + \dots}$$

where f_1 is first frequency, h_1 is first height; etc.

[1] i.e. Number of families in which this occurs.
[2] The height given is the mid point of the interval; e.g. 64 in. includes people from 5ft. 3in. to just under 5ft. 5in. in height.

CHAPTER ELEVEN

MENSURATION OF RECTANGULAR FIGURES

1. The Area of a Rectangle

Mensuration is the measurement of geometrical quantities, such as lengths of lines, areas of plane or curved surfaces, and volumes of solids.

In this chapter we shall consider *rectangular* plane figures and solids, and applications of these shapes to problems.

A rectangle is a plane figure, popularly known as an oblong, having the properties that its opposite sides are equal in length and parallel to one another, and all its angles are right angles.[1] If all the sides of the rectangle are equal, then the figure is a square.

If we have a square, 1 in. long and 1 in. broad, we say that its area is 1 *square inch (sq. in.)*.

Suppose now that we have a rectangle ABCD, 4 in. long and 3 in. broad. Draw lines 1 in. apart dividing it into 1-in. squares as shown. Each row contains 4 squares, but there are 3 rows.

∴ The number of squares = 4 × 3 = 12 squares, and we say that the area is 12 sq. in.

In general if the length of a rectangle is *l* in. and its breadth is *b* in., its *area = l × b sq. in.* . . (1)

In formula (1) if the area is *A* sq. in., we have

$$A = l \times b$$
$$\therefore l \times b = A$$

---

[1] A *minimum* definition of a rectangle is much more restricted than this.

$$\text{so } l = \frac{A}{b} \text{ and } b = \frac{A}{l}$$

on dividing both sides by either b or l.

In words: Length $= \dfrac{\text{Area of Rectangle}}{\text{Breadth}}$ . . (2)

Breadth $= \dfrac{\text{Area of Rectangle}}{\text{Length}}$ . . (3)

The formulæ (1), (2) and (3) are all the same really, but the subject of the formula (i.e. the unknown quantity to be found) has been changed.

2. Perimeter

The *perimeter* of *any* figure is the length round the edge.

In rectangle PQRS, the perimeter is
PQ + QR + RS + SP
$= l + b + l + b$
$= 2l + 2b$
$= 2(l + b)$

In words, *the perimeter of a rectangle* is twice the sum of its length and breadth.

The perimeter of a *circle* is the length of its circumference, and is $2\pi r$ (where r is the radius), as we shall see later. The perimeter of a *polygon* (a figure bounded by straight lines) is the sum of the lengths of its sides.

Ex. 1. Find the perimeter and area of a rectangle 6 ft. long and 5 ft. wide.

$$\begin{aligned}
\text{Area} &= \text{Length} \times \text{Breadth} \\
&= 6 \times 5 \text{ sq. ft.} \\
&= \textbf{30 sq. ft.} \\
\text{Perimeter} &= 2 \, (\text{Length} + \text{Breadth}) \\
&= 2 \, (6 + 5) \text{ ft.} \\
&= \textbf{22 ft.}
\end{aligned}$$

Ex. 2. Find the area of a rectangle 2 ft. 4 in. by 3 ft. 2 in.

$$l = 2 \text{ ft. } 4 \text{ in. } = 28 \text{ in.}$$
$$b = 3 \text{ ft. } 2 \text{ in. } = 38 \text{ in.}$$
$$\therefore A = l \times b \quad = 28 \times 38 \text{ sq. in.}$$
$$= \textbf{7 sq. ft. 56 sq. in.}$$

```
        38
        28
       ---
       304
        76
144|1064|7
      1008
       ----
        56
```

Note that we divide by 144 because there are 144 sq. in. in 1 sq. ft.

EXERCISE 1

Find the areas of rectangles with the following dimensions (questions 1–6):

1. 7 in. long, 10 in. wide
2. 1 ft. long, 2 ft. 6 in. wide
3. 17 cm. long, 24 cm. wide
4. 3 yd. by 21 in. (in square feet).
5. 2 ft. 7 in. long, 3 ft. 8 in. high
6. 2 ch. 10 yd. by 14 yd. (in square yards).
7. Find the area of a square of side 16 ft., in square yards and square feet.
8. Find the perimeters in questions 1–6 above.
9. The area of a rectangle is 24 sq. ft. If it is 3 ft. long, what is its perimeter?
10. A rectangular room is of area 200 sq. ft. If its breadth is 12 ft. 6 in., what is its length?
11. A field is of area 2½ acres and is of rectangular shape. The length of one side is 55 yd. Find the length of the other sides, and also its perimeter.
12. A rectangle has a perimeter of 38 in. One side is of length 10 in. Find its area.

3. Applications to Plane Figures

If we wish to find the cross-sectional area of a body, such as the casting illustrated, it is easily found by dividing the area up into rectangles, as indicated by dotted lines.

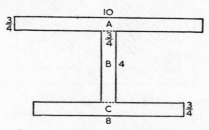

(Measurements are given in inches.)

Area required $= A + B + C$

$\qquad = 10 \times \frac{3}{4} + 4 \times \frac{3}{4} + 8 \times \frac{3}{4}$ sq. in.

$\qquad = (10 + 4 + 8) \times \frac{3}{4}$ sq. in.

$\qquad = \dfrac{22 \times 3}{4}$ sq. in.

$\qquad = \mathbf{16\frac{1}{2}}$ **sq. in.**

When we have a piece removed from a lamina (i.e. a plane body like a piece of plywood, of almost negligible thickness), or if we wish to calculate, say, the area of a lawn surrounding a flower-bed, we subtract the removed (or inside) area from the whole area. We do not divide the remaining area into small rectangles, as this leads to unnecessary labour.

Ex. 3. A path of width 2 ft. 6 in. is to be laid round a rectangular lawn 25 ft. by 14 ft. Calculate the area of the path. (See diagram overleaf.)

Length of whole garden $= 25 + 2\frac{1}{2} \times 2 = 30$ ft.
Breadth of whole garden $= 14 + 2\frac{1}{2} \times 2 = 19$ ft.

$\therefore$ Total area (path + lawn) $= 30 \times 19 = 570$
$\qquad\qquad$ Area of lawn $= 25 \times 14 = \underline{350}$
$\therefore$ Required area of the path $\qquad\qquad = \mathbf{220}$ **sq. ft.**

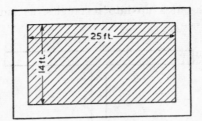

Note that we add twice the width of the path in assessing the whole length and whole breadth.

Ex. 4. Find the cost of fertilising a rectangular lawn 49 ft. by 21 ft. with fertiliser bought in packets each costing 1s. 3d., if a packet will cover 12 sq. yd.

$$\text{Area of lawn} = 49 \times 21 \text{ sq. ft.}$$
$$\text{Area covered by packet} = 12 \text{ sq. yd.} = 12 \times 9 \text{ sq. ft.}$$

$$\therefore \text{No. of packets required} = \frac{49 \times \overset{7}{2\!\!\!/1}}{\underset{3}{12 \times 9}}$$

$$= \frac{343}{36} = 9\tfrac{19}{36}.$$

∴ *10 packets are required*, as shopkeepers are loath to sell $\tfrac{19}{36}$ of a packet.

∴ Total cost = 10 × 1s. 3d. = **12s. 6d.**

A particularly useful application of area of a rectangle is the assessment of the quantity of wallpaper required to paper a room, or the amount of distemper needed for a ceiling.

A *"piece"* of wallpaper is 12 yd. long and 21 in. wide. Its area is therefore $36 \times \tfrac{7}{4}$ sq. ft., i.e. **63 sq. ft.** The room to be decorated should be thought of as having the walls laid out flat. (length = l ft., breadth = b ft., height = h ft.)

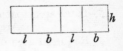

The total length = perimeter of room
$$= 2 \, (l + b) \text{ ft.}$$
∴ Area of walls = Total length × height
$$= \text{Perimeter} \times \text{height}$$
$$= \mathbf{2 \, (l + b) \, h. \, sq. \, ft.}$$

Although it is not customary to paper doors or windows, there is no necessity to deduct their areas from the quantity of paper estimated, unless they are very large. The difference is useful in making up for wastage. Another practical point is to remember to allow extra for matching patterned paper from one strip to the next!

EXERCISE 2

1. Find the areas of the given figures. All the angles are right-angles.

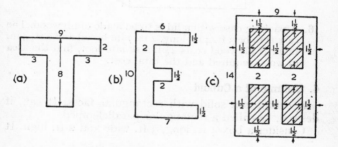

All the measurements in this question are in inches. The shaded areas have been cut out.

2. A photograph 10 in. by 9 in. is placed inside a frame of overall size 12 in. by 10 in. What is the uncovered area surrounding the photograph?

3. A lawn is 34 ft. by 27 ft. Two rectangular flowerbeds are cut in it, each of size 8 ft. by 7 ft. 6 in. What is the area of the lawn remaining? How many turves 3 ft. by 1 ft. would be needed to cover this remaining area of lawn, and what would be their cost at 4d. each?

4. A rectangular room is 16 ft. 6 in. long and 11 ft. 9 in. wide. Its height to the picture rail is 7 ft. 6 in. Calculate the area of the four walls and find the number of pieces of wallpaper required to cover the walls.

If, now, it were decided to paper the end walls with paper of one kind and the side walls with paper of another sort, would it be necessary to order more paper? How many pieces of each sort would be needed?

5. The diagram represents a rectangular box. If all the external faces are to be painted except the base, what is the area to be dealt with? (Answer in square feet.)

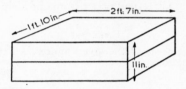

6. A packing case with a lid is to be made of plywood. The case is to be 3 ft. 4 in. long, 2 ft. 7 in. broad and 2 ft. 5 in. high. If plywood costs $4\frac{1}{2}$d. a square foot, find the area of wood required and the total cost.

4. Volume of a Cuboid

A *cuboid* is a solid with rectangular faces. It can, if desired, be called a rectangular parallelepiped.

Consider a box 4 ft. long, 3 ft. wide and 2 ft. high. It

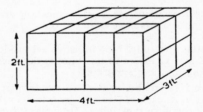

can be imagined as divided up into a number of cubes each 1 ft. × 1 ft. × 1 ft., i.e. each of volume 1 cu. ft.

The top layer has 4×3 of these cubes, and the second layer has the same. ∴ Altogether there are $4 \times 3 \times 2$ cubes, i.e. **24 cubes,** but the volume of each cube is 1 cu. ft. ∴ Volume of cuboid = **24 cu. ft.**

This result can clearly be extended to a cuboid of length l ft., breadth b ft. and height h ft., giving

$$\text{Volume of cuboid} = \textbf{l} \times \textbf{b} \times \textbf{h cu. ft.}$$
$$= (l \times b) \times h$$
$$= \textbf{Area of base} \times \textbf{height}$$

If we call the volume, V cu. ft.,

$$l \times b \times h = V$$

$$\therefore h = \frac{V}{l \times b} \text{ (or more shortly } \frac{V}{lb}\text{)}.$$

$$\text{i.e. } \textbf{h} = \frac{\textbf{V}}{\textbf{A}} \text{ (where } A \text{ is the base area).}$$

(This last formula, $h = \dfrac{V}{A}$ applies to many solids which are not cuboids. It does in fact apply to prisms in general. Thus, the formula $V = A \times h$ is of widespread use—e.g. in calculating the volume of material in a girder of given cross-sectional area and length.)

Ex. 5. The volume of a tank is 240 cu. ft. Its length and breadth are 8 ft. and 9 ft. respectively. Find its height.

$$\text{Height} = \frac{\text{Volume}}{\text{Length} \times \text{Breadth}}$$
$$= \frac{240}{8 \times 9} \text{ ft.} = 3\tfrac{1}{3} \text{ ft.} = \textbf{3 ft. 4 in.}$$

Ex. 6. How many bricks 9 in. $\times$ $4\tfrac{1}{2}$ in. $\times$ 3 in. are required to build a wall 20 ft. long, 5 ft. 6 in. high and 9 in. thick (ignoring thickness of mortar)?

$$\text{Volume of brick} = 9 \times 4\tfrac{1}{2} \times 3 \text{ cu. in.}$$
$$\text{Volume of wall} = 20 \times 12 \times 66 \times 9 \text{ cu. in.}$$

$$\therefore \text{Number of bricks} = \frac{20 \times 12 \times 66 \times 9}{9 \times 4\frac{1}{2} \times 3}$$

$$= \frac{20 \times 12 \times 66 \times 9 \times 2}{9 \times 9 \times 3}$$

$$= \frac{3520}{3} = 1173\frac{1}{3}$$

i.e. **1174 bricks are required.**

Notes. (1) Simplification is delayed into the end. (2) The actual number of bricks required in practice would have to be greater, as some are cut. One might perhaps add 5% to the final answer.

5. The Box

In assessing the volume of material used in making a box, there is a point to bear in mind when thickness of material cannot be neglected. If the box has a lid, there are two thicknesses of material in each direction. If there is no lid, there is only one thickness, in a vertical direction (assuming the box is standing on its base).

We would normally know the external dimensions of the box and the thickness of material.

Consider the lidless box shown. The external length, breadth and height are L, B, H respectively.

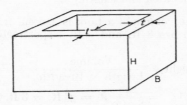

Suppose the thickness of the wood used is t (*measured in the same units as L, B and H*).

External length $= L$, Internal length $= L - 2t$
External breadth $= B$, Internal breadth $= B - 2t$
External height $= H$, Internal height $= H - t$

∴ External volume = LBH

Internal volume   = $(L - 2b) (B - 2t) (H - t)$

∴ Volume of material used

$$= \mathbf{LBH} - (\mathbf{L} - \mathbf{2t}) (\mathbf{B} - \mathbf{2t}) (\mathbf{H} - \mathbf{t})$$

If the box had had a lid, then

Volume of material used

$$= \mathbf{LBH} - (\mathbf{L} - \mathbf{2t}) (\mathbf{B} - \mathbf{2t}) (\mathbf{H} - \mathbf{2t})$$

where H in this case is measured to the top of the lid, when closed.

Ex. 7. Find the volume of material used in making a box, without a lid, of external measurements 4 ft. long, 3 ft. broad, 1 ft. 10 in. high. The wood is $\frac{1}{2}$ in. thick.

$$L = 48 \text{ in.} \qquad \therefore L - 2t = 47 \text{ in.}$$
$$B = 36 \text{ in.} \qquad B - 2t = 35 \text{ in.}$$
$$H = 22 \text{ in.} \qquad H - t = 21\tfrac{1}{2} \text{ in.}$$

∴ Volume required

$$= (48 \times 36 \times 22 - 47 \times 35 \times 21\tfrac{1}{2}) \text{ cu. in.}$$
$$= (38016 - 35367\tfrac{1}{2}) \text{ cu. in.}$$
$$= 2648\tfrac{1}{2} \text{ cu. in.}$$
$$= \mathbf{1 \text{ cu. ft. } 920\tfrac{1}{2} \text{ cu. in.}}$$

EXERCISE 3

1. A tank is 13 ft. 6 in. long and 12 ft. 4 in. wide. It contains water to a depth of 6 ft. Find in cubic yards the volume of water in the tank. Also find its weight if water weighs $62\frac{1}{2}$ lb. per cubic foot.

2. Water flows into a tank of length 6 ft. and breadth 4 ft. How long will it take the water level to rise 2 ft. in the tank if the rate of flow is 25 gall. per minute? (1 cu. ft. = $6\frac{1}{4}$ gall.)

3. A sheet of metal is 3·2 metres long and 1·25 metres wide. It weighs 168 kilograms. If the metal weighs 10·5 grammes per cubic centimetre, find the thickness of the sheet in millimetres.

4. A quarter of an inch of rain falls on a one-acre field. Calculate the weight of the water which has fallen, if water weighs $62\frac{1}{2}$ lb. per cubic foot. (Give the answer in tons.)

5. Find the volume of wood required to make a box of internal dimensions 2 ft. 3 in., 1 ft. 9 in. and 1 ft. 6 in., if the wood is $\frac{1}{2}$ in. thick, and the box is to have a lid.

6. A path 36 yd. long is to be laid in a garden. If the width of the path is 4 ft., find the cost of covering it with gravel to a depth of 3 in., if gravel costs 17s. 6d. a cubic yard.

6. The Area of a Triangle

Suppose we have triangle ABC (the symbol for triangle is $\triangle$).

Construct a rectangle BCDE on the same base BC and of the same height as $\triangle$ ABC, then DE passes through A. Draw AX perpendicular to BC.

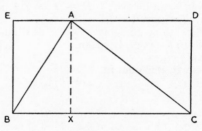

FIG. 1.

The diagonal line AB divides rectangle AEBX into two equal parts.

$$\therefore \triangle ABX = \tfrac{1}{2} \text{ rect. } AEBX^{1} \qquad . \qquad . \qquad . \qquad (1)$$

Similarly $\triangle ACX = \tfrac{1}{2}$ rect. ADCX $\qquad . \qquad . \qquad (2)$

In fig. 1 *add* these
$$\therefore \triangle ABC = \triangle ABX + \triangle ACX$$
$$= \tfrac{1}{2} \text{ rect. } AEBX + \tfrac{1}{2} \text{ rect. } ADCX$$
$$= \tfrac{1}{2} \textbf{ rect. BCDE.}$$

---

[1] The sign of equality is here taken to mean "equal in area."

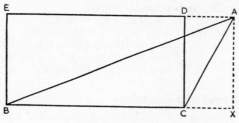

FIG. 2.

In fig. 2 subtract (2) from (1).

$$\therefore \triangle \text{ABC} = \triangle \text{ABX} - \triangle \text{ACX}$$
$$= \tfrac{1}{2} \text{ rect. AEBX} - \tfrac{1}{2} \text{ rect. ADCX}$$
$$= \tfrac{1}{2} \textbf{ rect. BCDE.}$$

Both cases give the same result. Now area of rect. BCDE = BC × DC, but this is the same as BC × AX.

$$\therefore \triangle \text{ABC} = \tfrac{1}{2} \text{ BC} \times \text{AX}$$
$$= \tfrac{1}{2} \textbf{ base} \times \textbf{ height}$$
$$= \tfrac{1}{2} \textbf{ bh (if base} = b \text{ units, height} = h \text{ units).}$$

Ex. 8. Find the area of the side of the lean-to green-house shown.

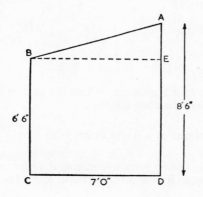

Draw BE perpendicular to AD.

AE = 8 ft. 6 in. − 6 ft. 6 in. = 2 ft.

Area of ABCD = △ ABE + rect. BCDE
$$= \tfrac{1}{2} \times BE \times AE + BE \times ED$$
$$= \tfrac{1}{2} \times 7 \times 2 + 7 \times 6\tfrac{1}{2} \text{ sq. ft.}$$
$$= 7 + 45\tfrac{1}{2} = \mathbf{52\tfrac{1}{2} \text{ sq. ft.}}$$

7. The Area of a Trapezium

A *trapezium* is a quadrilateral (four-sided figure) with *one* pair of opposite sides parallel.

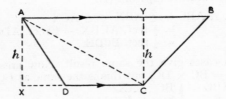

In the trapezium ABCD, join AC and draw AX perpendicular to CD produced, and CY perpendicular to AB.

Let AB = a, CD = b, AX = YC = h (because AB is parallel to DC).

Area of trapezium = △ ABC + △ ADC
$$= \tfrac{1}{2} AB \times CY + \tfrac{1}{2} DC \times AX$$
$$= \tfrac{1}{2} ah + \tfrac{1}{2} bh$$
$$= \tfrac{1}{2} (\mathbf{a} + \mathbf{b}) \mathbf{h.}$$

∴ **Area of a trapezium = half the sum of the parallel sides × their distance apart.**

8. The Volume of a Right Prism

A right *prism* is a solid of uniform cross-section, the end sections being perpendicular to the generating edges. A greenhouse is prismatic in shape, and so is a girder.

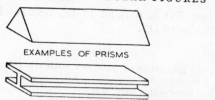

EXAMPLES OF PRISMS

The Volume of a prism = area of cross-section × le gth.

Ex. 9. Find the area of the given figure, ABCDE. Angles A, C and D are right angles.

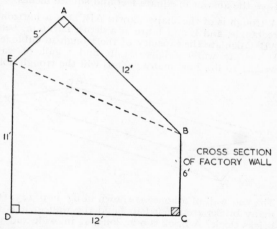

CROSS SECTION OF FACTORY WALL

Join EB.
Area of figure ABCDE
= Area of △ ABE + Area of trapezium BCDE
= $\frac{1}{2}$ AB × AE + $\frac{1}{2}$ (BC + ED) × DC
= {$\frac{1}{2}$ × 12 × 5 + $\frac{1}{2}$ (6 + 11) × 12} sq. ft.
= 30 + 102 = **132 sq. ft.**

Notice that we take AB as base of △ ABE, so that AE is its height, because AE is perpendicular to AB.

Further, ED is parallel to BC because both are perpendicular to DC.

EXERCISE 4

1. Find the areas of triangles with the following measurements:
   (a) base 6 in., height 9 in.
   (b) base 2·5 cm., height 3·6 cm.

2. A triangle is of area 112 sq. in. and its height is 1 ft. 2 in. Find the length of its base.

3. Calculate the area of a trapezium in which the parallel sides are 3 ft. 3 in. and 4 ft. 7 in. and are 2 ft. 1 in. apart. Give the answer in square feet and square inches.

4. A trough is of the shape shown. ABCD is a horizontal rectangle, and E and F are at a depth 1 ft. 6 in. below AB. Calculate the capacity of the trough in cubic feet. If 1 cu. ft. water weighs 62½ lb. and 1 gall. of water weighs 10 lb., how many gallons will the trough hold?

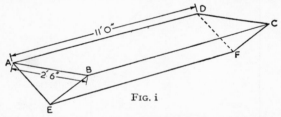

FIG. i

5. The end wall of a house is shown in fig. ii, p. 123. How many bricks are needed to build the wall, if it is two bricks thick? A brick is 9 in. long, 4½ in. wide and 3 in. deep and it is laid flat, so that there is 3 in. (including cement or mortar) between successive courses.[1]

6. Find the weight of a girder made of steel if it is 20 ft. long and is of cross-sectional area shown. All the angles in the figure are right angles. Steel weighs 480 lb. per cu. ft. (fig. iii, p. 123).

[1] In practice, as bricks are not cut with diagonal corners, some extra would be ordered to cover wastage. See note (2) on page 116.

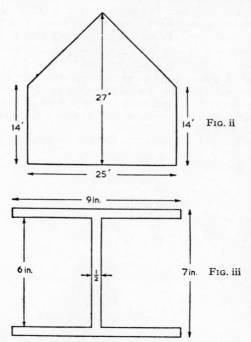

Fig. ii

Fig. iii

9. Square Root

The *square root* of a given number N is a number y which, when multiplied by itself, gives N. That is

$$y \times y = N$$
i.e. $$y^2 = N$$

y is the square root of N. It is written

$$\mathbf{y} = \sqrt{\mathbf{N}}.$$

Some numbers have exact square roots, e.g.

$$\sqrt{9} = 3 \text{ (because } 3 \times 3 = 9).$$

The sequence of numbers 1, 4, 9, 16 . . . which are *perfect squares* have exact square roots, 1, 2, 3, 4 . . . .

Most numbers do not have exact square roots. Consider $\sqrt{3}$. $1 \times 1 = 1$, $2 \times 2 = 4$ ∴ $\sqrt{3}$ lies between 1 and 2. Trying again we have $1.7 \times 1.7 = 2.89$ and $1.8 \times 1.8 = 3.24$, so more accurately $\sqrt{3}$ lies between 1.7 and 1.8. Now it would be very tedious to find square roots by trial-and-error methods such as this. There is, however, a simple way of finding square roots as accurately as we wish.

We will illustrate this method by examples.

Ex. 10. Find $\sqrt{66049}$

```
              2   5   7
             ─────────────
(i)   2     │6  60  49
            │4
            │
(ii)  45    │2  60
            │2  25          ∴ √66049 = 257.
            │
(iii) 507   │   35  49
            │   35  49
            │
            │   .....
```

In this example the square root is exact. In the next, it is not. The steps are as follows.

(*a*) Pair off the numbers *both ways* from the decimal point *if there is one. If not, pair off from the right-hand end.* [e.g. 6 60 49.]

(*b*) Find the largest number which, when multiplied by itself, does not exceed the first paired group. (In this case 6.) The number is 2, for $2 \times 2 = 4$. 3 would have been too big, for $3 \times 3 = 9$. Put the 2 on the top line and at (i).

(*c*) Subtract the result 4 from 6. $6 - 4 = 2$. Bring down the next *pair* 60, making 260.

(*d*) Double the 2 at (i) and write the result at (ii).

Find the largest number which can be written after the 4 at (ii), and the result multiplied by this new number to give a number smaller than 260. The number is 5, because 45 × 5 = 225. The number 6 would have been too big, for 46 × 6 = 276, which is bigger than 260. Put the 5 on top and next to the 4 at (ii).

(e) Subtract 225 from 260. 260 − 225 = 35. Bring down the next *pair* 49, making 3549.

(f) Double the *last figure only* of the 45 at (ii) and re-write at (iii). Result is 40 + 5 × 2 = 50. Find the largest number which can be written after the 50 and the result multiplied by this new number to give a number which will not exceed 3549. The number is 7, because 507 × 7 = 3549 exactly.

Ex. 11. Find $\sqrt{3}$ correct to 3 decimal places.

	1· 7 3 2 0
1	3·00 00 00 00
	1
	—
27	2·00
	1 89
343	11 00
	10 29
3462	71 00
	69 24
3464	1 76 00

∴ Correct to 3 decimal places, $\sqrt{3} \backsimeq$ **1·732.**

The determination of the position of the decimal point requires care. For the student who is learning from a book of this nature, probably the best method is to make a rough approximation. Suppose we wish to find the square root of 0·447.

Now we get $\sqrt{0·447}$ equal to 66 8 . . .(by the process already indicated) with a decimal point somewhere; but

0·6 × 0·6 = 0·36 and 0·7 × 0·7 = 0·49. ∴ √0·447 lies between 0·6 and 0·7. ∴ √0·447 = **0·668** . . ..

Multiplication of a number by 100 multiplies the square root by 10. Division of a number by 100 implies division of the square root by 10. Take care to avoid the common mistake √2 = 1·4142. ∴ √0·2 = 0·14142. The number 2 has been divided by 10, so that its square root should have been divided by √10, i.e. by 3·162. The actual value of √0·2 is 0·4472.

Ex. 12. Find √0·00635, correct to 3 decimal places.

From the above:

```
              0· 0  7   9   6
   0   │ 0·00 63  50  00
   7   │      49
  ──   │      ──
 149   │      14  50
       │      13  41
       │      ──  ──
1586   │       1  09  00
       │          95  16
```

Check: 0·07 × 0·07 = 0·0049; 0·08 × 0·08 = 0·0064.
∴ √0·00635 = 0·0796 . . .. ≏ **0·080 (3 d.p.)**.

EXERCISE 5

Find the square roots of the following numbers, exactly:

1. 5329   **2.** 925444   **3.** 9096256.

Evaluate the following, correct to 4 significant figures:

4. √2   **5.** √16·83   **6.** √4·937
7. √219·9   **8.** √6423   **9.** √0·397
10. √0·0584   **11.** √0·00756   **12.** √0·000773.

10. Pythagoras' Theorem and Right-angled Triangles

Suppose we have triangle ABC with a right-angle at C. The side opposite the right-angle is called the hypotenuse. Let the length of the sides opposite angles A, B, C be *a*, *b*, *c* units respectively.

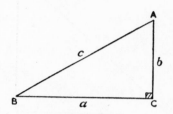

Pythagoras' Theorem states that the square on the hypotenuse of a right-angled triangle is equal to the sum of the squares on the other two sides.

In our diagram, $\mathbf{c^2 = a^2 + b^2}$.
If, for example, $a = 4$ in., $b = 3$ in.
then $c^2 = 4^2 + 3^2$
$= 16 + 9 = 25$
$\therefore c = \sqrt{25} = \mathbf{5\ in.}$

A right-angled triangle such as this, wherein the three sides are integral, i.e. are whole numbers, is called Pythagorean.

Other examples of Pythagorean triangles are:

(a) 5, 12, 13: for $5^2 + 12^2 = 13^2$
(b) 8, 15, 17: for $8^2 + 15^2 = 17^2$.

Ex. 13. Find the longest side of a right-angled triangle in which the other sides are 1 ft. and 2 ft.

Let the length be x ft.

$\therefore x^2 = 1^2 + 2^2 = 5$
so $x = \sqrt{5} = \mathbf{2 \cdot 236\ ft.}$

Ex. 14. Find a in the given figure, in which AC = 15 ft., BC = 11 ft. and angle ABC = 90°.

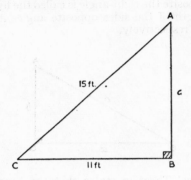

We have $a^2 + 11^2 = 15^2$

$$\therefore a^2 = 225 - 121 = 104$$
$$\therefore a = \sqrt{104}$$
$$= 10 \cdot 2 \text{ ft.}$$

Ex. 15. A lean-to greenhouse has end sections as shown. The shaded area indicates the height to which bricks are used in its construction, the rest being covered with glass in steel supports. The greenhouse is 9 ft. long. Calculate the volume of air in the greenhouse. Also find the area of glass required in its construction, neglecting the thickness of the steel.

Cross-sectional area of greenhouse

$$= \tfrac{1}{2} (5\tfrac{1}{2} + 7\tfrac{1}{2}) \times 6 \text{ sq. ft.}$$
$\therefore$ Its volume $= \tfrac{1}{2} \times 13 \times 6 \times 9$ cu. ft.
$$= \textbf{351 cu. ft.}$$

Area of glass = Area of front + 2 × Area of End + Sloping Roof Area.

Now AB is found by Pythagoras' Theorem, by drawing AC perpendicular to the wall.

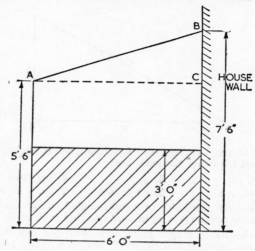

$$AB^2 = AC^2 + BC^2 = 6^2 + (7\tfrac{1}{2} - 5\tfrac{1}{2})^2$$
$$= 36 + 4 = 40$$
$$\therefore AB = \sqrt{40} = 6 \cdot 325$$

Sloping roof area

$$= 9 \times 6 \cdot 325 \qquad\qquad = \quad 56 \cdot 925 \text{ sq. ft.}$$

Area of front

$$= 9 \times (5\tfrac{1}{2} - 3) = 9 \times 2 \cdot 5 = \quad 22 \cdot 5 \quad\text{ sq. ft.}$$

2 × Area of Glass End

$$= 2 \times \tfrac{1}{2}(2\tfrac{1}{2} + 4\tfrac{1}{2}) \times 6 \qquad = \quad 42 \cdot 0 \quad\text{ sq. ft.}$$

$$\therefore \text{ Total area of glass} = 121 \cdot 425 \text{ sq. ft.}$$
$$\eqsim \mathbf{121 \text{ sq. ft.}}$$

EXERCISE 6

1. In the triangle ABC, angle C is a right-angle. Find the value of the unknown side in each of the following cases:

   (a) $a = 20$, $b = 21$ (b) $c = 37$, $a = 35$
   (c) $a = 11$, $c = 61$ (d) $a = 45$, $b = 28$.

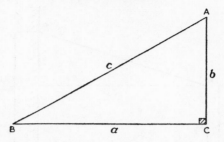

Find the hypotenuses of right-angled triangles, given
that the other two sides are:

2. 63, 16   **3.** 3, 7   **4.** 9·4, 16·8
5. 209, 476   **6.** 93·5, 46·8 **7.** 0·86, 0·72

8. Find the third side of a right-angled triangle in which
the hypotenuse is 23 in. and one side is 16 in.

9. A ladder of length 22 ft. rests with one end on horizontal ground and the other against a vertical wall. If
the distance of the foot of the ladder from the bottom
of the wall is 5 ft., find how far up the wall the ladder
reaches. (Answer in feet and inches, to nearest inch.)

10. The figure ABCD represents the end section of a shed.
Angles C and D are right angles. If BC = 6 ft., AD =
8 ft. 6 in. and AB = 7 ft., calculate CD and the area of
ABCD.

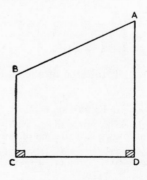

11. Calculate the cost of making the shed in question 10, if it is 8 ft. long, and if it is to be made entirely of planks 6 in. wide. There is no floor, and the cost of the planks is 4d. a foot run.[1]

12. Find the length of the side of a square field of area 1 acre, correct to the nearest foot. (Answer in chains, yards and feet.)

13. A pyramid VABCD has a square base ABCD and vertex V. VA = VB = VC = VD = 7 in. AB = 4 in. Calculate the height of the vertex above the base, correct to 4 significant figures.

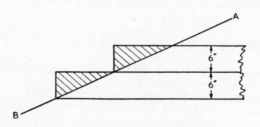

[1] It is worth observing that rather more timber would be needed in practice, to allow for cutting end sections of shed along line AB.

CHAPTER TWELVE

LOGARITHMS

1. Indices

In Chapter 3 brief reference was made to the idea of an index. It is now necessary to investigate this concept a little more closely.

Consider 4×8. We know that $4 = 2^2$, $8 = 2^3$

$$\therefore 4 \times 8 = 2^2 \times 2^3 = 2.2.\ 2.2.2$$
$$= 2^5$$

Also $27 \times 81 = 3^3 \times 3^4 = 3.3.3.\ 3.3.3.3$
$$= 3^7.$$

In each of the above, the final index is found to be the sum of the original indices: $2 + 3 = 5$; $3 + 4 = 7$.

This suggests that when we multiply two numbers together, if we could express them as *powers* of some other number (powers of 2 or 3 in the above examples), then we could replace the process of *multiplying* the original numbers by the simpler process of *adding* the *indices* of the new numbers.

Now this is not a very helpful idea unless there is some easy way of (*a*) converting the original numbers to powers of some other number (called the *base*), *and* (*b*) converting the result (2^5 or 3^7 in the above examples) back into an ordinary number. Fortunately, however, there exist sets of tables for this very purpose. The method by which they are constructed is quite simple but is outside the scope of this book.

The *base* which we use in logarithmic work in arithmetic is the number 10, as this accords with our decimal system of counting. It is not, however, the only base in general use,[1] but it will suffice for our needs. Logarithms

---

[1] Logarithms are first calculated, in making up tables, to the base $e = 2·71828 \ldots$. Logarithms to the base e are called Naperian logarithms, after their inventor, Napier.

to the base 10 are called common, or Briggian, logarithms.

e.g. $10^2 \times 10^3 = 10^5$.
Now $10^2 = 100$, $10^3 = 1000$, $10^5 = 100000$.

2, 3, 5 are called the logarithms of 100, 1000, 100000 respectively to the base 10. They can be written

$2 = \log_{10} 100$, $3 = \log_{10} 1000$, $5 = \log_{10} 100000$.

We now need 4 important formulæ. If x and y are any numbers,

$$10^x \times 10^y = 10^{x+y} \qquad . \qquad . \qquad . \qquad (1)$$
$$10^x \div 10^y = 10^{x-y} \qquad . \qquad . \qquad . \qquad (2)$$
$$(10^x)^y = 10^{xy} \qquad . \qquad . \qquad . \qquad (3)$$
$$\sqrt[y]{10^x} = 10^{x/y} \qquad . \qquad . \qquad . \qquad (4)$$

We shall not attempt the general proof of these formulæ but shall verify them for a few simple cases.

We have already seen that $10^2 \times 10^3 = 10^5$ which verifies (1).

Now $10^6 \div 10^4 = \dfrac{10.10.10.10.10.10}{10.10.10.10} = 10^2$ which verifies (2) as $6 - 4 = 2$.

$(10^3)^2 = (10.10.10)(10.10.10) = 10^6$ which verifies (3) as $3 \times 2 = 6$.

$\sqrt[3]{10^6} = \sqrt[3]{(10.10)(10.10)(10.10)} = 10^2$ which verifies (4) as $\frac{6}{3} = 2$.

There is a particular case of great importance. It is the value to be assigned to 10^0.

Now by (1), $10^2 \times \boxed{10^0} = 10^{2+0} = 10^2$ if (1) is to hold in this case,
but $10^2 \times \boxed{1} = 10^2$ as multiplication by one does not alter the value of a quantity.
$\therefore$ 10^0 must be defined as 1.

We then have the following basic table.

Number	Logarithm (to base 10)
1	0
10	1
100	2
1000	3
10000	4

. . . (5)

etc.

We observe that the *logarithm* of each of these numbers is one less than the number of whole *digits* in it. This is important, as will be seen later.

So far we have confined ourselves to numbers which are whole powers of ten. We must now extend our ideas to cover intermediate numbers.

2. Graphical Considerations

Let us construct a graph of the function $y = 10^x$, i.e. the graph in which x is the logarithm of y to the base 10.

Using table (5) above, and plotting the values of x (the *logarithms* 0, 1, 2, 3 . . .) along the horizontal axis, and the values of y (the *numbers* 1, 10, 100 . . .) along the vertical axis, we get a set of points (0, 1), (1, 10), (2, 100), (3, 1000) as shown. It is necessary to use different scales for x and y because of the rapid increase in y.

Join up the points by a smooth curve, and we can then read off the logarithms of intermediate values.

For example, log 800 $\eqsim$ 2·9, that is $800 = 10^{2·9}$.

The graph clearly shows that *every number between*:

1 and   10 has a logarithm between 0 and 1;
10 and   100 has a logarithm between 1 and 2;
100 and 1000 has a logarithm between 2 and 3 etc.

Now $800 = 8 \times 100 = 10^2 \times 8$, so if $8 = 10^x$, we can see that $10^2 \times 10^x = 10^{2·9}$. Therefore $x = \textbf{0·9}$.

∴ The logarithm of 8 differs from the logarithm of

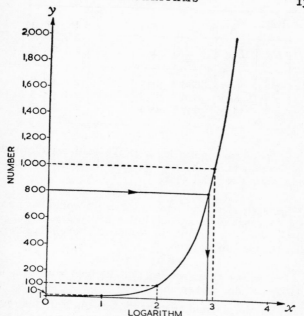

800 only by its whole number part. This idea is perfectly general:

The logarithm of any number consists of:

(I) A whole number part, called the *characteristic*, which depends only on the number of figures before the decimal point in the given number;

(3) A decimal part, called the *mantissa*, which depends on the actual figures present, irrespective of the position of the decimal point.

3. Logarithms

Turn to the table of logarithms, part of which is reconstructed on page 136.

2·313		↓ B	C		P	Q	↓ R	
	A							
No.	Log	1	2	...	1	2	3	...
2·3	·3617	**3636**	3655		2	4	**6**	
2·4	·3802	3820	3838		2	4	5	
2·5	·3979	3997	4014		2	3	5	

FIG. 2

Suppose we require log 2·4. We read 2·4 down the left-hand side. In the column under Log, headed A, *and opposite* 2·4 we read 3802.

$$\therefore \log 2·4 = 0·3802.$$

Similarly if we had wanted log 24 we would have used the same *mantissa* (·3802), but a new *characteristic* (1), determined by the rule in section 2 above, because 24 lies between 10 and 100.

$$\therefore \log 24 = 1·3802.$$

Proceeding thus, we see that log 240 = 2·3802, log 2400 = 3·3802 and so on.

When the given number has three significant figures in it, such as 2·42, we read the first two numbers, as before, down the left-hand side; but now read off the result under the column, headed C, for the third figure (2) in 2·42.

$$\therefore \log 2·42 = 0·3838, \log 24·2 = 1·3838, \log 242 = 2·3838 \text{ etc.}$$

If the number were, say, 2·51, we would read 2·5 down the side and pick out ·3997 under the column for 1 (headed B). $\therefore \log 2·51 = 0·3997.$

Finally, when the given number has four significant figures, such as 2·313, we read off the first two down the left-hand side and the third in its appropriate column (in this case 1, headed B). This gives 0·3636. The fourth figure is entered in the *mean difference column*, in the same row as before, and under the column for this fourth figure (in this case 3, column R) we read off 6.

So we have

No.	Log
2·313	0·3636
	+ 6
	0·3642

We add the figure obtained (in the above it is 6) to the last figure in the mantissa, as shown. The arrows in fig. 2 should make the procedure clear.

A brief explanation may be helpful.

$$\left.\begin{array}{l} \log 2\cdot31 = 0\cdot3636 \\ \log 2\cdot32 = 0\cdot3655 \end{array}\right\} \text{The difference is } 0\cdot0019.$$

Now 2·313 is $\frac{3}{10}$ of the way from 2·31 to 2·32. We may therefore conjecture that log 2·313 is very near $\frac{3}{10}$ of the way from 0·3636 to 0·3655; but $\frac{10}{10}$ represents a move of 0·0019.

∴ $\frac{3}{10}$ represents a move of $\frac{3}{10} \times 0\cdot0019 = 0\cdot00057 \frown 0\cdot0006$ to 4 decimal places, and this is the figure which we obtained from the mean difference column.

This process of estimating the difference between one number and another and calculating a fraction of this difference is called *interpolation*. It is a powerful mathematical method, widely used in statistical and actuarial work.

A few examples are now shown, using the logarithm table on pages 226-7. The student should verify them for himself. He should learn to add differences (where necessary) mentally as soon as possible.

No.	Log	No.	Log
4·7	0·6721	8·647	0·9369
8	0·9031	92·36	1·9655
2·97	0·4728	104·9	2·0207

EXERCISE 1

1. Find the logarithms of the following numbers:

(a) 6	(b) 9·2	(c) 31	(d) 1·64
(e) 7·25	(f) 6·48	(g) 86·2	(h) 19·7
(i) 4·845	(j) 32·41	(k) 317·2	(e) 1·048
(m) 164,000	(n) 9·897	(o) 5450	(p) 70·98.

2. Draw the graph of $y = \log x$ from $x = 1$ to $x = 10$, taking the values of x as follows:

x	1	2	3	4	5	6	7	8	9	10
$y = \log x$	0	·3010	·4771	·6021						1

Firstly complete the above table, then, taking the x-axis as horizontal, mark off the values of x half an inch apart on graph paper. Mark each half-inch on the y-axis as 0·1 units as indicated in the sketch. Join the points obtained from the table above by a smooth curve.

When completed, from your graph read off the values of:[1]

$$\log 6\cdot5, \quad \log 3\cdot7, \quad \log 8\cdot3;$$

and also the numbers whose logs are 0·42, 0·59, 0·20.

Check your results from the table of logarithms.

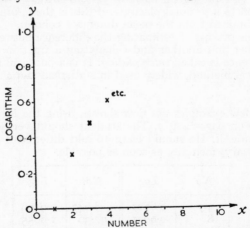

[1] It should be possible to get the result accurate to 2 decimal places.

4. The Four Rules of Logarithms

The four formulæ (1), (2), (3), (4) given in section 1 above constitute the four rules of logarithms.

    I. When we wish to *multiply* two numbers, we *add* their logarithms.

    II. When we wish to *divide* one number by another, we *subtract* the logarithm of the denominator from that of the numerator.

    III. When we wish to find the yth power of a number, we *multiply* the logarithm by this power, y.

    IV. When we wish to find the yth root of a number, we *divide* the logarithm by y.

Some examples will soon make this clear, but we must first find how to use the *antilogarithm table*.

Suppose we wish to find 3.624×18.5.

No.	Log	
3·624	0·5592	from the logarithm table
18·5	1·2672	
+	**1·8264**	using rule I.

Now this is only of value if we can find the number whose logarithm is 1·8264. That is, we require the *antilogarithm* of 1·8264. Turn to the antilogarithm tables on pages 228–9. Below is the required part for this example.

·8264										
Log	0	...	5	6	...	1	2	3	4	...
·81	6457		6531	6546		2	3	5	6	
·82	6607		6683	**6699**		2	3	5	**6**	
·83	6761		6839	6855		2	3	5	6	

In using the antilogarithm table, *only the mantissa is entered*, i.e. 0·8264. Remember that the characteristic, 1 in this example, only determines the position of the decimal point in the answer. We enter the table in

exactly the same way as before in all other respects;
·82 down the left-hand side, 6 along the top, 4 in the
difference column, as indicated by the arrows.

Entry ·8264; antilog is 6699 + 6 = 6705.

To determine the position of the decimal point, note
that by section 2 above 1·8264 is the logarithm of a
number between 10 and 100.

∴ Antilog 1·8264 = **67·05,** and this is the required
result.

EXERCISE 2

1. Find the antilogarithms of the following:

(a) 0·6154	(b) 0·3047	(c) 0·8995	(d) 0·0019
(e) 1·2700	(f) 1·0809	(g) 2·4677	(h) 4·6021
(i) 0·9879	(j) 0·7788	(k) 3·4186	(l) 5·5109.

Ex. 1. Find the value of 1·986 × 2·324.

No.	Log	Rule I.
1·986	0·2980	
2·324	0·3662	
+	0·6642	Antilog 0·6642 = **4·615.**

Ex. 2. Find the value of 327·9 ÷ 71·8.

No.	Log	Rule II.
327·9	2·5157	
71·8	1·8561	
−	0·6596	Antilog 0·6596 = **4·566.**

Ex. 3.   Calculate $\dfrac{3·947 \times 86·43}{93·77}$

No.	Log	
3·947	0·5963	Rule I
86·43	1·9367	
+	2·5330	Rule II
93·77	1·9720	
−	0·5610	Antilog 0·5610 = **3·639.**

Ex. 4. Evaluate $(3\cdot942)^4$.

No.	Log	
3·942	0·5957	Rule III
× 4	2·3828	Antilog 2·3828 = **241·4**.

Ex. 5. Find the cube root of 71·2.

No.	Log	
71·2	1·8525	Rule IV
÷ 3	0·6175	∴ $\sqrt[3]{71\cdot2}$ = **4·145**.

For emphasis, we repeat the following rules:

A. Numbers between   1 and   10 have *characteristic* 0
    „   „   10 and 100   „   „   1
    „   „   100 and 1000   „   „   2
                                                      etc.

B. Only the *mantissa* is used in the tables themselves.

$$\log 63\cdot8 = \mathbf{1\cdot8048}$$

CHARACTERISTIC_____↑ ↑_____MANTISSA

Exercise 3

Find the values of the following expressions:

1. 3·47 × 9·18   **2.** 61·3 × 2·054   **3.** 322 × 2·76

4. 1·048 × 32·95   **5.** 3·646 × 1·922   **6.** 307·4 × 296·6

7. 38·4 ÷ 9·77   **8.** 6·029 ÷ 5·73   **9.** 3724 ÷ 717

10. 3985 ÷ 21·76   **11.** 36·88 ÷ 9·828   **12.** 67500 ÷ 43·84

13. $\dfrac{6724 \times 1\cdot925}{837\cdot1}$ **14.** $\dfrac{3\cdot28 \times 6\cdot95}{12\cdot74}$ **15.** $\dfrac{214\cdot6 \times 38\cdot7}{61\cdot5 \times 9\cdot212}$

16. $\sqrt{24\cdot9}$ **17.** $\sqrt[5]{8\cdot637}$ **18.** $(21\cdot95)^3$

19. $(6\cdot009)^4$ **20.** $\sqrt[4]{(17\cdot28)^3}$ (multiply the log by 3 and divide the result by 4).

5. Negative Characteristics

The student will probably have noticed that hitherto we have restricted ourselves to numbers greater than 1. Suppose, however, we require the logarithm of a number less than 1, say 0·6248. Before we can discuss this in detail it is necessary to consider powers of ten again.

Rule (1) in Section 1 gave us

$$10^x \times 10^y = 10^{x+y}$$

Suppose now that $x = 4$ and $y = -1$.

$$\therefore 10^4 \times \boxed{10^{-1}} = 10^3$$
$$\text{but we know } 10^4 \times \boxed{\tfrac{1}{10}} = 10^3$$

so therefore 10^{-1} and $\tfrac{1}{10}$ must be the same quantity.

We infer that
$$10^{-1} = \tfrac{1}{10} = 0·1$$
$$10^{-2} = \tfrac{1}{100} = 0·01$$
$$10^{-3} = \tfrac{1}{1000} = 0·001 \text{ etc.}$$

∴ The logarithms of numbers which lie between 0 and 1 are always negative.

Now we know that $0·6248 = 6·248 \times \tfrac{1}{10}$.

∴ log $0·6248$ = log $6·248$ + log $\tfrac{1}{10}$, but we have seen that the log $\tfrac{1}{10} = -1$ from above.

∴ log $0·6248 = ·7958 - 1$

$$= \bar{1}·7958.$$

We put the minus over the characteristic to show that this is negative, but that the mantissa is not. It is really a short way of writing $-1 + ·7958$.

Similarly log $0·06248 = ·7958 - 2$

$$= \bar{2}·7958$$
$$\text{log } 0·006248 = ·7958 - 3$$
$$= \bar{3}·7958 \text{ and so on.}$$

We can now extend rule A in section 3 above:

Numbers between

100 and 1000	have characteristic	2 etc. . . .
10 and 100	,,	,,	1
1 and 10	,,	,,	0
0·1 and 1	,,	,,	$\bar{1}$
0·01 and 0·1	,,	,,	$\bar{2}$
0·001 and 0·01	,,	,,	$\bar{3}$ etc. . . .

Ex. 6. Find the logarithms of 0·82, 0·00471, 0·005228.

No.	Log
0·82	$\bar{1}$·9138
0·00471	$\bar{3}$·6730
0·005228	$\bar{3}$·7184

EXERCISE 4

1. Find the *characteristics* of the logarithms of the following numbers:

    (a) 3·94   (b) 0·7287   (c) 31950   (d) 0·000622
    (e) 0·093854   (f) 0·00006   (g) 0·01008.

2. Find the logarithms of the following numbers:

    (a) 0·2194   (b) 0·063   (c) 21776   (d) 0·0009526
    (e) 0·09091   (f) 0·8637   (g) 0·00000062.

3. Find the antilogarithms of the following:

    (a) 2·645   (b) $\bar{2}$·645   (c) $\bar{1}$·9837   (d) $\bar{4}$·727
    (e) 6·9   (f) $\bar{3}$·9289   (g) $\bar{1}$·0099   (h) $\bar{7}$·7687.

Manipulation with negative characteristics requires care. Their difficulties are best illustrated by examples.

Ex. 7. Multiply 0·6284 by 0·739.

No.	Log
0·6284	$\bar{1}$·7983
0·739	$\bar{1}$·8686
+	$\bar{1}$·6669
	1

∴ 0·6284 × 0·739 = **0·4644.**

The point to observe here is that the carrying figure to the characteristics column is positive, whilst the characteristics are themselves negative.

∴ $\bar{1} + \bar{1} + 1 = \bar{1}$, for this is the same as $-1 - 1 + 1 = -1$.

Ex. 8. Multiply 0·0094 by 21·3.

No.	Log
0·0094	$\overline{3}$·9731
21·3	1·3284
+	$\overline{1}$·3015

Antilog $\overline{1}$·3015 = **0·2002.**

Here, $\overline{3} + 1 + 1 = \overline{1}$.

Ex. 9. Evaluate 6·205 ÷ 0·8381.

No.	Log
6·205	0·¹7927
0·8381	$_1\overline{1}$·9233
−	0·8694

Antilog 0·8694 = **7·403.**

We borrow +1 from the bottom characteristic so that we can get 1·7 − ·9 = 0·8. Paying it back makes the bottom characteristic −1 + 1 = **0.**

∴ Final characteristic = 0 − 0 = 0.

(Alternatively, putting it in full,

$$0·7927 - (-1 + ·9233) = 0·7927 + 1 - ·9233$$

on changing the sign of everything inside the bracket, giving 1·7927 − 0·9233 = 0·8694.)

Ex. 10. Find the value of (0·862)³.

No.	Log
0·862	$\overline{1}$·9355
× 3	$\overline{1}$·8065

∴ (0·862)³ = **0·6404.**

In this case $3 \times \overline{1} = \overline{3}$, add 2, giving $\overline{1}$.

Ex. 11. Find the value of $\sqrt[4]{0·0729}$

No.	Log
0·0729	$\overline{2}$·8627
÷ 4	$\overline{1}$·7157

∴ $\sqrt[4]{0·0729}$ = **0·5196.**

We cannot divide 4 into $\overline{2}$ and get a whole number, so we proceed as follows:

$$\overline{2}{\cdot}8627 \div 4 = (\overline{4} + 2{\cdot}8627) \div 4 = \overline{1} + {\cdot}7157.$$

The characteristic is always made into an exact multiple of the divisor.

Ex. 12. Evaluate $\sqrt{\dfrac{31{\cdot}46 \times 7{\cdot}92}{3940 \times 0{\cdot}86}}$

No.	Log
31·46	1·4977
7·92	0·8987
+	2·3964
→	3·5300
−	$\overline{2}$·8664
÷ 2	$\overline{1}$·4332 ⟶ Antilog $\overline{1}$·4332 = **0·2711.**
3940	3·5955
0·86	$\overline{1}$·9345
+	3·5300

We (1) add the numerator logs; (2) add the denominator logs; (3) subtract the second result from the first; (4) divide the result by two to get the square root of the original expression.

EXERCISE 5

Find the values of the following expressions:

1. $3{\cdot}82 \times 0{\cdot}463$ **2.** $0{\cdot}89 \times 0{\cdot}414$

3. $2{\cdot}68 \times 0{\cdot}19 \times 3{\cdot}045$ **4.** $0{\cdot}0024 \times 0{\cdot}4891$

5. $(0{\cdot}938)^2$ **6.** $\sqrt{0{\cdot}09745}$

7. $(2{\cdot}91)^3 \times 0{\cdot}003635$ **8.** $(0{\cdot}0912)^2 \div 0{\cdot}8477$

9. $6{\cdot}328 \div 17{\cdot}914$ **10.** $0{\cdot}915 \div 214{\cdot}3$

11. $0{\cdot}00385 \div 0{\cdot}001767$ **12.** $164 \div (0{\cdot}928)^2$

13. $\dfrac{61{\cdot}42 \times 3{\cdot}098}{2{\cdot}94 \times 0{\cdot}8087}$ **14.** $\dfrac{21{\cdot}38}{(0{\cdot}645)^2 \times 319{\cdot}7}$

15. $\sqrt{\dfrac{0{\cdot}625}{0{\cdot}38 \times 5{\cdot}752}}$ **16.** $\sqrt[3]{(0{\cdot}8228)^4}$.

6. Harder Problems and Applications to Formulæ

The student will by now have realised the power of
logarithmic work to simplify difficult calculations.
There are, however, certain pitfalls to be avoided.

$$\text{Consider } \frac{3\cdot624}{8\cdot041} + \frac{0\cdot283}{0\cdot914}.$$

The difficulty about this seemingly harmless expression
is the plus between the two quotients. We have to work
out each quotient separately, and to make it perfectly
clear the example is worked below.

No.	Log	No.	Log
3·624	0·5592	0·283	$\bar{1}$·4518
8·041	0·9054	0·914	$\bar{1}$·9609
—	$\bar{1}$·6538		$\bar{1}$·4909

$$\text{Antilog } \bar{1}\cdot6538 \quad 0\cdot4506$$
$$\text{Antilog } \bar{1}\cdot4909 \quad 0\cdot3096$$
$$+ \quad \mathbf{0\cdot7602}$$

The antilogarithm of each part must be taken before
the final addition. The same care must be exercised
when there is a minus between two expressions.

Let us now consider the accuracy of our answers. The
tables which we have been using are four-figure tables.
We have to appreciate therefore that the fourth figure is
not usually exactly correct, but is an approximation.
For example log 2 = 0·30103 . . . is given in the tables
as log 2 = 0·3010. If however we work out 2^3 by logs we
get the following:

No.	Log
2	0·3010
× 3	0·9030 →Antilog 0·9030 = **7·998**.

Now we know perfectly well that $2^3 = 8$, so there is an
error of 0·002 in the answer given by the logarithm

tables. If we corrected the answer to *three significant figures* we should get 7·998 ⌒ 8·00, which is correct.

We can, therefore, expect that, in using four-figure tables, our answer will be *correct to three significant figures*, except when long and involved expressions or high powers (e.g. 3^{14}) occur. In this case the answer may be accurate only to two significant figures.

From now on we shall carry out all working to four significant figures and correct the answer to three significant figures.

Formulæ form an integral part of the modern world, especially in engineering and scientific work. Many people need to gain speed and accuracy in calculating certain results by substituting known values of given quantities in a formula and evaluating the expression so obtained. Three possible methods can be considered:

(1) Long calculation. This has been discussed in detail earlier.
(2) Logarithms.
(3) Slide Rule. This is a valuable method and is discussed in detail in "Teach Yourself the Slide Rule", uniform with this book.

When the problem involves elaborate working or considerable accuracy, the use of logarithms is best. Four-figure tables are not the only ones in general use. Inman's Nautical Tables, used in the Royal Navy for navigational work, are five-figure tables. Norie's Tables, used in the Merchant Service, are six-figure tables. There are sets of seven-figure tables in common use, e.g. Chambers' Mathematical Tables. There are also tables of greater accuracy.

Ex. 13. The time of oscillation of a compound pendulum is given by $T = 2\pi \sqrt{\dfrac{k^2}{lg}}$. Find T when $l = 3.5$, $g = 32.2$, $k = 2.94$.

No.	Log
2	0·3010
π	0·4971
2·94	0·4683
+	1·2664 (i)
3·5	0·5441
32·2	1·5079
+	2·0520
÷ 2	1·0260 (ii)
—	0·2404

We have

$$T = 2 \times \pi \times \sqrt{\frac{(2 \cdot 94)^2}{(3 \cdot 5)(32 \cdot 2)}}$$

$$= \frac{2 \cdot \pi \cdot (2 \cdot 94)}{\sqrt{(3 \cdot 5)(32 \cdot 2)}}$$

$$= 1 \cdot 74$$

(*Note.*—The final log, 0·2402, was obtained by subtracting (ii) from (i).)

EXERCISE 6

1. Evaluate $\dfrac{2 \cdot 71}{6 \cdot 38} - \dfrac{4 \cdot 197}{7 \cdot 925}$.

2. Simplify $\sqrt[3]{\dfrac{0 \cdot 925 \times 32}{761 \times 0 \cdot 008472}}$

3. If $T = 2\pi \sqrt{\dfrac{l}{g}}$, find T when $l = 7 \cdot 4$, $g = 32$.

4. The formula $v^2 = u^2 + 2fs$ occurs in the study of dynamics.
   Find (i) v, if $u = 17 \cdot 3$, $f = 0 \cdot 62$, $s = 86$
        (ii) s, if $u = 0$, $v = 38 \cdot 4$, $f = 0 \cdot 93$
       (iii) f, if $u = 61 \cdot 4$, $v = 80$, $s = 7 \cdot 75$.

5. The area of a triangle is given by the formula
   $\triangle = \sqrt{s(s-a)(s-b)(s-c)}$, where a, b, c are the lengths of the sides and s is the semi-perimeter (i.e. $s = \frac{1}{2}(a + b + c)$). Find $\triangle$, if $a = 7$, $b = 9 \cdot 4$, $c = 8 \cdot 6$.

6. The formula for a gas expanding under adiabatic conditions is $p = \dfrac{k}{v^{1 \cdot 4}}$, where p is the pressure and v is the volume.
   Find (i) k if $p = 10$ when $v = 6 \cdot 5$
       (ii) p when $v = 8 \cdot 74$ using the value of k just found.

7. The focal length of a lens is given by the formula
   $$\frac{1}{f} = \frac{1}{v} + \frac{1}{u}$$
   Find f if $u = 16 \cdot 3$, $v = 21 \cdot 8$.

8. Simplify $\dfrac{(61 \cdot 35)^2 - (42 \cdot 08)^2}{794 \cdot 6}$.

CHAPTER THIRTEEN

THE CIRCLE, CYLINDER, CONE AND SPHERE

1. Definitions: Properties of a Circle

A *circle* is a path traced out on a plane by a point moving so that its distance from a fixed point, called the *centre*, is always constant. This distance is called the *radius*, r, of the circle.

A *chord* of a circle is a straight line, such as CD in fig. 1, which terminates at the circle at both ends.

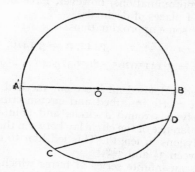

A *diameter* is a chord passing through the centre O. AB is a diameter, of length d, say. All diameters of a circle are equal and they are all bisected at O. Now OA = OB = r, as both are radii. ∴ AB = OA + OB = $2r$.

The *circumference* of a circle is the distance round its edge. It is equivalent to the perimeter of a polygon. We shall use C to stand for circumference.

One of the earliest references to an important property

of the circle occurs in the Bible (2 Chronicles iv, 2) and reads as follows: "Also he made a molten sea of ten cubits from brim to brim, round in compass, and five cubits the height thereof; and a line of thirty cubits did compass it round about."

Now this gives a circumference of 30 cubits for a circle of diameter 10 cubits, and leads to an early estimate of the ratio $\dfrac{\text{Circumference}}{\text{Diameter}}$ as being 3. *The ratio, circumference divided by diameter, is constant for all circles*, but the value 3 is a very rough approximation. More accurately, it is $3\frac{1}{7}$ (or $\frac{22}{7}$), a value often used today when great accuracy is not needed. The exact value of the ratio is π (pi). It is an incommensurable quantity, that is, one which cannot be estimated exactly. Very accurate approximations, however, have been made to hundreds of places of decimals.

Here are some approximations:

$$\pi = \tfrac{22}{7}, \pi = 3\cdot142, \pi = 3\cdot1416.$$

Actually $\pi = 3\cdot14159265358979323846\ldots$ to 20 decimal places.

Archimedes devised an ingenious method of approximation for π. He inscribed and circumscribed 96-sided regular polygons round a circle, and pointed out that the circumference of the circle lay between the perimeters of the polygons in length. This led him to deduce that π lay between $3\frac{1}{7}$ and $3\frac{10}{21}$.

There is an infinite series of terms which would give π exactly if we could sum the series. It is

$$\frac{\pi}{4} = 1 - \frac{1}{3} + \frac{1}{5} - \frac{1}{7} + \ldots$$

and is called Gregory's series, but it should be pointed out that many terms would have to be taken to give a reasonable value of π. This formula can be found easily by Integral Calculus. Other series giving π also exist.

In this book we shall take π as either $\frac{22}{7}$ or $3\cdot142$ according to our requirements. The former is often used when logarithms are not needed in the question, and the latter is used otherwise.

Now, $$\frac{\text{Circumference}}{\text{Diameter}} = \pi.$$

∴ **Circumference, C** $= \pi d = 2\pi r$ (because $d = 2r$).

The area of a circle is πr^2, that is, π multiplied by the square of the radius. This formula can also be obtained by calculus.

Akmes, an Egyptian, found quite a good approximation to the area of a circle, nearly 4000 years ago. He suggested that $\frac{8}{9}$ of the diameter be taken and the result squared. This is equivalent to taking π as 3·1605* instead of 3·1416.

Now, area of circle, $\text{A} = \pi r^2 = \pi\left(\dfrac{d}{2}\right)^2$, (as $r = \frac{1}{2}d$)

$$= \frac{\pi d^2}{4}.$$

So we can obtain the circumference and area of a circle, given either radius or diameter, but the student is advised always to use $\text{C} = 2\pi r$, $\text{A} = \pi r^2$ to avoid mistakes. He should therefore convert diameter to radius wherever necessary.

Ex. 1. Find the circumference and area of a circle of radius $3\frac{1}{2}$ in.

$\qquad r = 3\frac{1}{2}$ in. $\quad$ ∴ $\text{C} = 2\pi r$
$\qquad\qquad\qquad\qquad = 2 \times \frac{22}{7} \times \frac{7}{2}$ in.
$\qquad\qquad\qquad\qquad = \textbf{22 in.}$
$\qquad\qquad\qquad\quad \text{A} = \pi r^2$
$\qquad\qquad\qquad\qquad = \frac{22}{7} \times \frac{7}{2} \times \frac{7}{2}$ sq. in.
$\qquad\qquad\qquad\qquad = \textbf{38·5 sq. in.}$

When using logarithms, it is useful to remember that

* $\left(\dfrac{8}{9}d\right)^2 = \dfrac{64}{81}d^2$; comparing with $\dfrac{\pi}{4}d^2$ we have $\dfrac{\pi}{4} = \dfrac{64}{81}$. ∴ $\pi = \dfrac{256}{81} = 3\cdot1605$.

$\log \pi = 0.4971$. Actually if we look up $\log 3.142$ in the tables we get 0.4972, which is a little less accurate.

Ex. 2. Find the radius of a circle of area 1 sq. ft.

We have $\pi r^2 = 1$ sq. ft.

$= 144$ sq. in.

$\therefore r^2 = \dfrac{144}{\pi}$ sq. in.

so $r = \sqrt{\dfrac{144}{\pi}}$ in.

$= 6.772$ in.

$= \mathbf{6.77\ in.}$ (approx.).

No.	Log
144	2.1584
π	0.4971
—	1.6613
$\div 2$	**0.8307**

Ex. 3. A reel of thread is to be 100 yd. long. If the radius of the reel is 0.6 in., find how many turns there must be on the reel.

In a problem of this kind we take the radius as the *average* radius, neglecting the thickness of the thread.

Length of one turn

$= 2\pi r = 2\pi \times 0.6$ in.

$= 1.2\pi$ in.

Length of thread

$= 100$ yd. $= 3600$ in.

No.	Log
3000	3.4771
π	0.4971
—	**2.9800**

$\therefore$ Number of turns

$= \dfrac{\text{Length of thread}}{\text{Length of one turn}}$

$= \dfrac{3600}{1.2\pi} = \dfrac{\overset{3000}{\cancel{3600}}}{\underset{1}{\cancel{1.2\pi}}} = \dfrac{3000}{\pi}$

$= \mathbf{955\ turns.}$

EXERCISE 1

1. Find the circumferences of the circles whose radii are: (a) 1.4 in. (b) $10\frac{1}{2}$ in. (c) 4 in. (d) 3 ft. 6 in. $(\pi = \frac{22}{7})$.

2. Find the areas of the circles whose radii are:
(*a*) 4·2 cm. (*b*) 1 ft. 2 in. (*c*) 3 in. (*d*) 5 cm. ($\pi = \frac{22}{7}$)

3. A circle is of area 49 sq. in. Find its diameter and its circumference. ($\pi = 3\cdot142$.)

4. Find the diameter of a circle of area 34 sq. in.

5. What is the circumference of a circle of area 2 sq. ft. ?

6. A piece of rope is 88 ft. long. How many complete turns can be made round a drum of diameter 2 ft. 6 in. ? Neglect the thickness of the rope.

7. A bicycle wheel is of diameter 26 in. How many turns does it make in travelling one mile ?

8. In a bicycle there are 48 teeth on the sprocket wheel to which the pedals are attached. There are 18 teeth on the sprocket wheel which is fixed to the back wheel of the bicycle. How many times does the rider have to turn the pedals in travelling 1000 yd., if a bicycle wheel is of diameter 26 in. ?

2. The Cylinder

The name cylinder covers a fairly large field of solid bodies. We shall restrict our definition to the *right circular cylinder*.

A cylinder is a solid with circular ends and all its

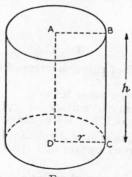

FIG. 2.

generating lines parallel. All its right sections are circles. It can be generated by revolving a rectangle round one of its edges (e.g. by revolving rectangle ABCD in fig. 2 about the line AD).

Let the base radius be r and the height be h, then *the volume* V is given by

$$V = \text{Base area} \times \text{height}$$
$$= \pi r^2 \times h$$
$$= \pi r^2 h.$$

The area of the curved surface of a cylinder is $2\pi rh$. This is easily proved. Suppose we wrap a piece of paper exactly once round the cylinder and then unroll it (fig. 3).

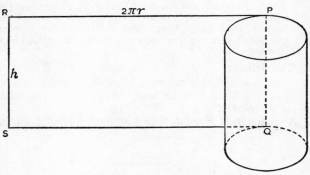

FIG. 3.

The length PR of paper unwrapped = Circumference of circle = $2\pi r$.

The height of the paper RS = h.

∴ Area of curved surface of cylinder = Area of rectangle PQSR = PR × RS = $2\pi r \times h = 2\pi rh$.

The *total surface area of a cylinder* is the sum of the areas of the curved surface and the two ends, so it is given by

$$2\pi rh + 2\pi r^2 = 2\pi r(r + h).$$

Ex. 4. Find the volume of a cylinder of diameter 6 in. and height 7 in. Find also its curved surface area.

We have $r = 3$ in., $h = 7$ in.

$$\therefore V = \pi r^2 h$$
$$= \tfrac{22}{7} \times 3 \times 3 \times 7 \text{ cu. in.}$$
$$= \textbf{198 cu. in.}$$

Curved surface area $= 2\pi r h$
$$= 2 \times \tfrac{22}{7} \times 3 \times 7 \text{ sq. in.}$$
$$= \textbf{132 sq. in.}$$

Ex. 5. Find how many square inches of copper are needed to make a can of radius $2\tfrac{1}{4}$ in. and height 6 in. The lid is to overlap the top of the can by $\tfrac{1}{2}$ in. (Neglect thickness of metal.)

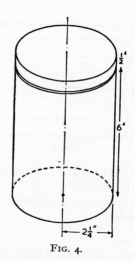

FIG. 4.

The area of metal required is the same as for a can of height $6\tfrac{1}{2}$ in.

$$\therefore \text{Total surface area} = 2\pi r(r + h)$$
$$= 2\pi \times 2\tfrac{1}{4} \times (2\tfrac{1}{4} + 6\tfrac{1}{2}) \text{ sq. in.}$$
$$= 2 \times \tfrac{22}{7} \times \tfrac{9}{4} \times \tfrac{35}{4} \text{ sq. in.}$$

$$= \overset{1}{\underset{1}{2}} \times \frac{\overset{11}{22}}{\underset{1}{7}} \times \frac{9}{\underset{1}{4}} \times \frac{\overset{5}{35}}{4} \text{ sq. in.}$$

$$= 123\tfrac{3}{4} \text{ sq. in.}$$

3. Material Used in Making a Pipe

A pipe can be thought of as two co-axial cylinders (i.e. cylinders with the same axis). It is easy to find the volume of material used by subtracting the inside volume from the whole volume.

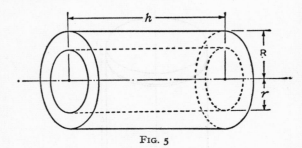

FIG. 5

Let R, r be the external and internal radii respectively. Then, volume of material

= Volume of larger cylinder—Volume of smaller cylinder

$= \pi R^2 h - \pi r^2 h$

$= \pi h(R^2 - r^2)$

The student who has done a little algebra will notice that $R^2 - r^2$ can be factorised into $(R + r)(R - r)$, and we have

Volume of material $= \pi h(R + r)(R - r)$

This is the form of answer most useful for logarithmic tables.

Sometimes the external radius, R, and *thickness*, t, are given, in which case $R - r = t$, whence $\mathbf{r} = \mathbf{R} - \mathbf{t}$, giving internal radius.

Ex. 6. Calculate the volume of material used in making a pipe of length 10 ft., external radius $\frac{1}{2}$ in. and thickness $\frac{1}{10}$ in.

$R = \frac{1}{2}$ in., $t = \frac{1}{10}$ in. Therefore $r = \frac{1}{2} - \frac{1}{10} = \frac{2}{5}$ in.; $h = 10$ ft. $= 120$ in.

$\therefore$ Volume of material $= \pi h(R^2 - r^2)$

$$= \tfrac{22}{7} \times 120 \times [\tfrac{1}{4} - \tfrac{4}{25}] \text{ cu. in.}$$
$$= \tfrac{22}{7} \times 120 \times \tfrac{9}{100} \text{ cu. in.}$$
$$= \mathbf{33 \cdot 9 \ cu. \ in.} \text{ (approx.).}$$

Ex. 7. A crucible is to be made in the form of a cylinder without a lid, the thickness of material being 1 in. throughout. The height is to be 14 in. externally, and the external radius is to be 8 in. If the material of which it is to be constructed weighs 450 lb. per cu. ft., find the weight of the crucible.

The point to bear in mind in this question is that the internal cylinder is of height 1 in. less than the external cylinder, as there is one end present.

If $R, H; r, h$ are external radius and height, internal radius and height respectively, we have $R = 8$ in., $r = 7$ in., $H = 14$ in., $h = 13$ in.

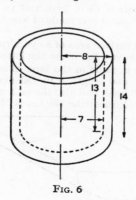

FIG. 6

Volume of material (actually iron)

$= \pi R^2 H - \pi r^2 h$ (a modified formula
$= \pi[8^2 \times 14 - 7^2 \times 13]$ cu. in. because of the differ-
$= \pi \times 259$ cu. in.   ence in the heights of
But 1 cu. ft. weighs 450 lb., i.e. the cylinders)
1728 cu. in. weigh 450 lb.

∴ Wt. of crucible

No.	Log
π	0·4971
259	2·4133
450	2·6532
+	5·5636
1728	3·2375
−	2·3261

$= \dfrac{259\pi}{1728} \times 450$ lb.

$= 211\cdot8$ lb.

$\simeq$ **212 lb.** (3 s.f.).

EXERCISE 2

1. A well of diameter 4 ft. has to be excavated to a depth of 56 ft. Find the volume of earth to be removed. (Answer in cubic yards.)

2. A cylindrical tank of radius 3 ft. is full of water. By how much does the water level fall if 25 gall. are drawn off? ($6\frac{1}{4}$ gall. = 1 cu. ft.)

3. A pipe is of external radius 8 in., and is made of material 1 in. thick. What is the volume of metal in a 6-ft. length of the pipe?

4. A telegraph pole is 18 ft. high and 10 in. in diameter. What is its weight if it is made of wood, weighing 36 lb. per cu. ft.?

5. Find the total surface area of a cylindrical can of height 9 in. and diameter 5 in., if the can has no lid.

6. A zinc trough is made in the form of half a cylinder of diameter 2 ft. and length 6 ft. Calculate the quantity of water it will hold, and also the area of zinc used in its manufacture. (Neglect the thickness of the zinc.)

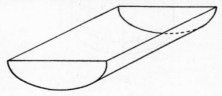

7. Calculate the volume of copper used in making a penny. (Make a heap of pennies and stand one against them, so estimating the average thickness of a penny.)

8. Water flows through a pipe of cross-sectional area 1 sq. in. at 8 ft. per sec. How long will it take to fill a tank of length 4 ft., breadth 2 ft. and height 3 ft.? (Think of cylinders of water 8 ft. long being put into the tank every second.)

4. The Cone

As with the cylinder, we shall limit our definition to the case of a *right circular* cone.

A cone is the solid formed by revolving a line about a fixed axis and always making a constant angle with it. (It can be thought of also as the solid formed by rotating △ VOA about VO in fig. 7.)

A cone has a circular base, centre O in fig. 7, and a *vertex*, V.

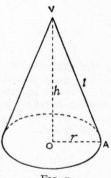

FIG. 7

The cone is a particular case of a pyramid, and its volume is given by:

$$\tfrac{1}{3} \times \text{Area of base} \times \text{height}$$
$$= \tfrac{1}{3} \times \pi r^2 \times h = \tfrac{1}{3}\pi r^2 h$$

i.e. it is one-third of the volume of a cylinder of the same radius and height.

There is another length which is important in the cone. It is the *slant height* VA = *l*. Now triangle OAV has a right angle at O, so by Pythagoras' Theorem, we have

$$VA^2 = VO^2 + OA^2$$
i.e. $l^2 = h^2 + r^2$.

The curved surface area of a cone is πrl.

This can be demonstrated by folding a piece of paper exactly once round the curved surface and unrolling it on a table. This gives a sector of a circle.

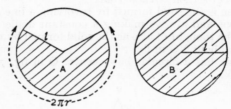

Fig. 8

Suppose we get the shaded area shown on the left, this being part of the circle shown on the right. The circle is of radius *l*. Now the length of arc (part of the circumference) in the left-hand circle was the circumference of base of cone, i.e. $2\pi r$. The length of circumference of the right-hand circle is $2\pi l$.

∴ In fig. 8:

$$\frac{\text{Area of A}}{\text{Area of B}} = \frac{\text{Length of arc of A}}{\text{Length of arc of B}}$$

$$\therefore \frac{\text{Area of A}}{\pi l^2} = \frac{2\pi r}{2\pi l} = \frac{r}{l}$$

$$\therefore \text{Area of A} = \frac{r}{l} \times \pi l^2 = \pi rl, \text{ as given above.}$$

(The area of a piece of cake is proportioned to its length of arc.)

Ex. 8. Find the curved surface and volume of a cone of height 4 in. and base radius 3 in.

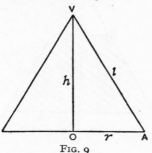

FIG. 9

$h = 4$ in., $r = 3$ in.

$$\therefore l^2 = 4^2 + 3^2 = 25 \text{ sq. in.}$$

$$\therefore l = \sqrt{25} = \textbf{5 in.}$$

$$\therefore \text{Curved surface} = \pi r l = \tfrac{22}{7} \times 3 \times 5 \text{ sq. in.}$$

$$= \textbf{47}\tfrac{1}{7} \textbf{ sq. in.}$$

$$\text{Volume} \quad = \tfrac{1}{3}\pi r^2 h$$

$$= \tfrac{1}{3} \times \tfrac{22}{7} \times 3 \times 3 \times 4 \text{ cu. in.}$$

$$= \textbf{37}\tfrac{5}{7} \textbf{ cu. in.}$$

More Difficult Example

Ex. 9. Find the area of crinothene used in making a lampshade in the form of a frustum of a cone, the upper and lower radii being 3 in. and 8 in. respectively and the slant height being 10 in.

A frustum of a cone is a section cut off by a plane parallel to its base.

Let V be the vertex. PQ, SR are upper and lower diameters of the frustum. The line VNO is perpendicular to the base.

Let $VQ = x$ in., then by similar triangles,[1]

$$\frac{VQ}{VR} = \frac{NQ}{OR}$$

[1] See "Teach Yourself Geometry", page 310, Theorem 58.

A.—8

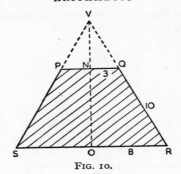

FIG. 10.

$$\therefore \frac{x}{x + 10} = \frac{3}{8}, \text{ giving } 8x = 3x + 30$$

$$\therefore 5x = 30$$
$$\text{so } x = \mathbf{6}.$$

∴ Curved surface of frustum

= Surface of cone VSR − Surface of cone VPQ
= $\pi RL - \pi rl$

where $R = 8$ in., $L = (x + 10)$ in. $= 16$ in., $r = 3$ in., $l = x$ in. $= 6$ in.

∴ Curved surface $= \frac{22}{7}(8 \times 16 - 3 \times 6)$ sq. in.
$= \frac{22}{7} \times 110$ sq. in.
$= \mathbf{345 \cdot 7}$ **sq. in.** (approx.).

EXERCISE 3

1. Find the volumes of right circular cones, given that:
   (a) base radius is 5 in., height is 7 in.
   (b) slant height is 13 in., base radius is 5 in.
   (c) slant height is 5 in., base radius is 1 in.

2. Find the curved surfaces of right circular cones of:
   (a) base radius 1·6 in., height 6·3 in.
   (b) height 3 in., slant height 4 in.
   (c) height 4 cm., radius of base 2 cm.

3. Find the total surface area of a cone of height 10 cm. and base diameter 6 cm.

4. Find the number of cubic feet of air in a conical tent of height 9 ft. and radius 7 ft. 6 in.

5. A heap of slag is in the form of a frustum of a cone, of upper and lower radii 20 ft. and 30 ft. respectively. The slant height of the heap is 15 ft. Estimate the weight of the slag, if it is taken that 1 cu. ft. weighs 400 lb. (Give the answer in tons, to the nearest ton.)

6. A solid steel cone of base radius 2 in., height 4 in. is dropped into a can partly filled with water. The can is a cylinder of radius 3 in. If the cone is totally submerged, and no water flows out of the cylinder, find the rise in water-level, to the nearest 0·01 in.

5. The Sphere

A *sphere* is traced out by a point moving so that its distance from a given point is constant. The definition is the same as for a circle except that the moving point is no longer restricted to a plane, but may move in space.

Alternatively we can think of a sphere as the solid generated by rotating a semicircle APB about its diameter AB.

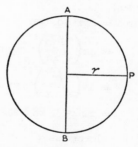

Fig. 11.

If r is the radius of the sphere, its *volume* = $\frac{4}{3}\pi r^3$ and its *surface area* = $4\pi r^2$.

These formulæ are obtained by calculus.

Ex. 10. Find the surface area and volume of a sphere of radius 2 in.

Volume

$$= \tfrac{4}{3}\pi r^3 = \tfrac{4}{3} \times \tfrac{22}{7} \times 2^3 \text{ cu. in.}$$

$$= \frac{4 \times 22 \times 8}{3 \times 7} \text{ cu. in.} = \mathbf{33 \cdot 5 \text{ cu. in.}}$$
(3 s.f.).

Surface area

$$= 4\pi r^2 = 4 \times \tfrac{22}{7} \times 2^2 \text{ sq. in.}$$

$$= \frac{88 \times 4}{7} \text{ sq. in.} = \mathbf{50 \cdot 3 \text{ sq. in.}} \text{ (3 s.f.)}$$

```
      88
       8 ×
   3)704
   7)234·66 ...
      33·52 ...

   7)352
      50·3
```

Ex. 11. The volume of a sphere is 10 c.c. Find its surface area.

If r cm. is the radius

$$\tfrac{4}{3}\pi r^3 = 10$$
$$\therefore 4\pi r^3 = 30$$

so $r^3 = \dfrac{30}{4\pi}$, giving $r = \sqrt[3]{\dfrac{30}{4\pi}}$

(We can work out r here or proceed to the end before doing so.)

Now Surface area $= 4\pi r^2$ sq. cm.

No.	Log
7·5	0·8751
π	0·4971
—	0·3780
÷ 3	0·1260
× 2	0·2520
4	0·6021
π	0·4971
+	**1·3512**

$$= 4\pi \left(\sqrt[3]{\frac{30}{4\pi}} \right)^2 \text{ sq. cm.}$$

$$= 4\pi \left(\sqrt[3]{\frac{7\cdot5}{\pi}} \right)^2 \text{ sq. cm.}$$

$$= 22 \cdot 45 \frown \mathbf{22 \cdot 5 \text{ sq. cm.}}$$

EXERCISE 4

1. Find the volumes and surface areas of spheres with the following radii:
   (a) 3·5 cm.   (b) 3 in.   (c) 1 in.   (d) 8·42 in.
2. A sphere is of volume 4 c.c. Find its radius.
3. The surface area of a sphere is 10 sq. in. What is its radius?
4. Find the surface area of a sphere of volume 12 cu. in.

5. A cube of metal, of side 8 in., is melted down and formed into 1000 ball bearings. What is the radius of the bearings?

6. A boiler consists of a cylinder of radius 4 ft. and length 10 ft. with hemispherical ends. What is the capacity of the boiler in cubic feet? (Answer to 3 significant figures.)

CHAPTER FOURTEEN

SIMPLE AND COMPOUND INTEREST

1. Simple Interest

When a sum of money is lent for a time some remuneration is made for the loan. This takes the form of *interest*, paid as a percentage of the sum loaned, called the *principal*.

For example, if a sum of money is deposited in a Post Office savings account, $2\frac{1}{2}\%$ interest is paid for each year that the money is lent. £200 deposited for one year would gain £5 interest.

Interest is paid also on deposits in banks, building societies and many other institutions.

The calculation of simple interest, I, is given by the formula

$$I = \frac{\text{Principal} \times \text{Rate per cent.} \times \text{Number of years}}{100}$$

or more shortly

$$I = \frac{P \times R \times N}{100} \text{ where} \begin{cases} P = \text{Principal in £'s} \\ R = \text{Rate per cent.} \\ N = \text{Number of years.} \end{cases}$$

Ex. 1. Find the simple interest on £500 for 3 years at 4% per annum.[1]

Principal = £500, Rate per cent. = 4, Number of years = 3.

$$\therefore I = \frac{P \times R \times N}{100}$$
$$= £\frac{500 \times 4 \times 3}{100}$$
$$= \textbf{£60.}$$

[1] For a year.

When the time for which the loan is made is a number of days, the value of N is given by $\dfrac{\text{Number of days}}{365}$, and the calculation will normally involve long multiplication and division and the use of decimals.

Ex. 2. Find the simple interest on £412 for 46 days at $3\frac{1}{4}\%$ per annum, to the nearest 1d.

$P = £412,\ R = 3\frac{1}{4},\ N = \frac{46}{365}.$

$$\therefore I = £\frac{412 \times 3\frac{1}{4} \times \frac{46}{365}}{100}$$

$$= £\frac{\overset{103}{412} \times 13 \times 46}{\underset{1}{100 \times 4 \times 365}}$$

$$= 1 \cdot 6875$$

$$= £1\ 13s.\ 9d.$$

	103
	13 ×
	1339
	46 ×
	8034
	5356
365	615·94	1·6875

```
       103
        13 ×
      1339
        46 ×
      8034
      5356
365 )615·94  1·6875
      365
      250·9
      219·0
       31·94
       29·20
        2·740
        2·555
         1850
         1825
```

Note.—Logarithms are not suitable for money problems as we need more than four figures in handling £ s. d.

```
1·6875
13·750
 9·0
```

2. Inverse Problems on Simple Interest

The formula $I = \dfrac{P \times R \times N}{100}$ involves four unknown quantities I, P, R, N, so if we are given any three we can find the fourth. To find any one of P, R, N it is convenient to rearrange the formula before using it.

We have

$$I = \frac{P \times R \times N}{100} \qquad . \qquad . \quad (1)$$

$$\therefore 100 \times I \qquad = P \times R \times N$$
$$\text{i.e. } P \times R \times N = 100 \times I \qquad . \qquad . \quad (2)$$

Dividing (2) by $R \times N$ we have

$$P = \frac{100 \times I}{R \times N} \qquad . \qquad . \quad (3)$$

Dividing (2) by $P \times N$ we have

$$R = \frac{100 \times I}{P \times N} \qquad . \qquad . \quad (4)$$

Dividing (2) by $P \times R$ we have

$$N = \frac{100 \times I}{P \times R} \qquad . \qquad . \quad (5)$$

The formulæ (3), (4) and (5) should be known, but it should be clearly understood that they are only variations of formula (1).

Ex. 3. What sum of money must be invested at $4\frac{1}{2}\%$ simple interest to give an interest of £90 in 5 years?

$R = 4\frac{1}{2}$, $I = £90$, $N = 5$.

$$\therefore P = \frac{100 \times I}{R \times N} = £\frac{100 \times 90}{5 \times 4\frac{1}{2}}$$

$$= £\frac{200 \times 90}{5 \times 9} = \textbf{£400.}$$

Ex. 4. For how long must £250 be invested at $2\frac{1}{2}\%$ per annum to give £50 simple interest?

$P = £250$, $I = £50$, $R = 2\frac{1}{2}$.

$$\therefore N = \frac{100 \times I}{P \times R} = \frac{100 \times 50}{250 \times 2\frac{1}{2}} = 8$$

$\therefore$ The time is **8 years.**

EXERCISE I

Find the simple interest due on the following investments:

	Principal	Rate per cent.	No. of years
1.	£400	6	3
2.	£285	2½	4
3.	£518	3½	5
4.	£6,400	4	2

Find the simple interest, to the nearest 1d., on:

5.	£274	3¼	2 years
6.	£489	5½	81 days
7.	£3055	4	175 days.

Find the missing items in the following table:

	Principal	Interest	Rate %	Time (years)
8.	x	£90	3	6
9.	£2400	£800	x	4
10.	x	£31 10s.	4½	3
11.	£1080	£432	5	x
12.	x	£17 5s.	3¼	5½

13. Jones pays £80 into the Post Office savings account and at the end of a year receives interest at 2½%. He pays this interest into the same account. How much interest will he get at the end of the next year?

14. Smith wishes to raise a mortgage on his house. The interest charged is 4½% per annum. If he can only afford to pay 18s. a week interest, how much money can he borrow? (It is to be assumed that the 18s. is interest only and does not include any repayment of capital.)

3. Compound Interest

The calculations made in simple interest are based on the assumption that the interest is paid in cash. It frequently happens, however, that the interest due is added to the principal at the end of each year, e.g. EXERCISE I,

No. 13 above. In such a case the second-year principal is greater than that of the first year, for

2nd-year principal = 1st-year principal + 1st-year interest

The quantity on the right is called the *amount after one year*.

Thus, if we call 1st, 2nd, 3rd . . . year principals P_1, P_2, P_3 . . . and 1st, 2nd, 3rd . . . year amounts A_1, A_2, A_3 . . . and the corresponding interests I_1, I_2, I_3 . . . then

$$P_2 = A_1 = P_1 + I_1$$
$$P_3 = A_2 = P_2 + I_2$$

Some examples will make this clear.

Ex. 5. Find the compound interest on £480 for 3 years at 5% per annum.

$$
\begin{array}{llr}
 & & £ \\
\left\{\begin{array}{l} P_1 \\ I_1 \end{array}\right. & \text{(5\% of } P_1) & \begin{array}{r} 480 \\ \underline{24} \end{array} \\
\left\{\begin{array}{l} P_2 = A_1 \\ I_2 \end{array}\right. & \text{(5\% of } P_2) & \begin{array}{r} 504 \\ \underline{25\cdot2} \end{array} \\
\left\{\begin{array}{l} P_3 = A_2 \\ I_3 \end{array}\right. & \text{(5\% of } P_3) & \begin{array}{r} 529\cdot2 \\ \underline{26\cdot46} \end{array} \\
A_3 & & \pounds555\cdot66
\end{array}
$$

Now A_3 is the amount for 3 years, so if we subtract from it the original principal P_1, we shall have the total interest added.

A_3	555·66	75·66
P_1	480·00	13·2
Compound interest ⟶	£75·66	2·4

i.e. **£75 13s. 2d.**

Notes

1. To find x% of a quantity move the decimal point two places to the left (thereby dividing by a hundred)

mentally and multiply by x, e.g. 3% of 742 (= 7·42 × 3) = 22·26.

2. The normal number of decimal places required during working is *five* (unless the steps are exact as in Ex. 5 above, in which case it is sometimes unnecessary to put down as many).

Ex. 6. Find the amount of £238 16s. 7d. for 2 years at 4% per annum.

	£		12) **7**·00000
P_1	238·82917		20)**16**·58333
I_1 (4% of P_1)	9·55316		**238**·82917
P_2	248·38233		
I_2 (4% of P_2)	9·93528		**258**·31761
A_2	**£258·31761**		**6**·3522
			4·2264

∴ Required amount is **£258 6s. 4d.**

When the interest is a quantity like $3\frac{1}{2}$%, we find 3% of the principal and $\frac{1}{2}$% separately and add the results. The $\frac{1}{2}$% can be found either as $\frac{1}{200}$ of the principal (involving moving the decimal point two places to the left mentally and dividing by two), or as $\frac{1}{6}$ of 3% (for $\frac{1}{2}$ is $\frac{1}{6}$ of 3).

Ex. 7. Find by how much the compound interest exceeds the simple interest on £843 for 2 years at $3\frac{1}{2}$% per annum.

		£
P_1		843·00
I_1	$\begin{cases} 3\% \\ \frac{1}{2}\% \end{cases}$	25·29
		4·215
P_2		872·505
I_2	$\begin{cases} 3\% \\ \frac{1}{2}\% \end{cases}$	26·17515
		4·36253
A_2 (amount for 2 years)		903·04268
less P_1		843·00000
Compound Interest		**£60·04268**

$$\text{Simple interest} = \frac{843 \times 2 \times 3\frac{1}{2}}{100}$$

$$= \text{£59·01}$$

$$843 \times 7 = 5901$$

$\therefore$ Compound interest — Simple
   interest

$$= \text{£}(60 \cdot 04268 - 59 \cdot 01)$$
$$= \text{£}1 \cdot 03268$$
$$= \text{£1 0s. 8}d. \text{ (to nearest 1}d.\text{)}.$$

$$\begin{array}{r} 1\cdot03268 \\ \overline{0\cdot6536} \\ \overline{7\cdot8432} \end{array}$$

It will be observed that the method used above is *practice*, and on occasion it can be tedious. In section 4 below an alternative method of great practical importance is discussed. When the number of years is great, practice methods are useless and the use of tables is essential.

Errors which arise in calculation by the method of the present section (i.e. section 3) can sometimes be spotted by noting that the successive values of the interest I increase fairly steadily.

EXERCISE 2

Find the compound interest on the following loans:

	Principal	Rate per cent. p.a.[1]	No. of Years
1.	£640	5	2
2.	£1750	4	3
3.	£184	2	4
4.	£1938	3½	2
5.	£643	4½	3

6. Find the compound interest on £720 for 2 years at 3% per annum, payable half-yearly. (In this case, take half the interest rate, 1½%, and add it in every half-year, i.e. 4 times in all.)

7. Find by how much the compound interest exceeds the simple interest on:
   (a) £400 for 2 years at 3% per annum.
   (b) £2750 for 3 years at 5½% per annum.

([1] per annum)

4. Compound Interest Formula

We saw that the second-year principal was the same as the first-year amount, i.e. $P_2 = A_1$, but

$A_1 = P_1 + P_1 \times \dfrac{r}{100}$ (for it is P_1 plus $r\%$ of P_1).

$$\therefore P_2 = A_1 = P_1\left(1 + \frac{r}{100}\right)$$

$$\text{Also } A_2 = P_2\left(1 + \frac{r}{100}\right)$$

$$= P_1\left(1 + \frac{r}{100}\right)\left(1 + \frac{r}{100}\right)$$

$$= P_1\left(1 + \frac{r}{100}\right)^2$$

Proceeding in this way we see that the amount for n years, A_n, is given by

$$\mathbf{A}_n = \mathbf{P}\left(1 + \frac{r}{100}\right)^n . \quad . \quad . \quad (1)$$

where P is the original principal and r is the rate per cent. per annum.

If we put $R = 1 + \dfrac{r}{100}$ in equation (1) we get the alternative formula

$$\mathbf{A} = \mathbf{P.R}^n \quad . \quad . \quad . \quad (2)$$

The quantity R is called the amount of £1 for 1 year, for if we put $n = 1$, $P = £1$ in equation (1) we get

$$A = £\left(1 + \frac{r}{100}\right).$$

The formula (2) is of considerable value in calculating A, especially when n is a large number of years. The value of R^n can be obtained from a set of tables such as those on page 174:

AMOUNT OF £1 AT COMPOUND INTEREST

Years	2½%	3%	3½%	4%	5%
1	1·0250000	1·0300000	1·0350000	1·0400000	1·0500000
2	1·0506250	1·0609000	1·0712250	1·0816000	1·1025000
3	1·0768906	1·0927270	1·1087179	1·1248640	1·1576250
4	1·1038129	1·1255088	1·1475230	1·1698586	1·2155062
5	1·1314082	1·1592741	1·1876863	1·2166529	1·2762816
10	1·2800845	1·3439164	1·4105988	1·4802443	1·6288946
20	1·6386164	1·8061112	1·9897889	2·1911231	2·6532977
30	2·0975676	2·4272625	2·8067937	3·2433975	4·3219424

Ex. 8. Find the amount of £650 for 10 years at 3½%.
Reading off the value of R^n in the row opposite 10
years and in the column under 3½%, we get
$R^n = $ 1·4105988.

∴ Required amount A
= £650 × 1·4105988
= £916·88922
= **£916 17s. 9d.**

$$
\begin{array}{r}
14·105988 \\
65 \times \\
\hline
70·529940 \\
846·35928 \\
\hline
\mathbf{916}·88922 \\
\hline
17·7844 \\
9·4128 \\
\end{array}
$$

It will be observed that, although 7-figure tables are
used, these are not of too great an accuracy when
multiplying by sums of money which run into hundreds
or thousands of pounds.

5. Compound Interest by Logarithms

Consider again the equation A = PR^n

$$\left(\text{where } R = 1 + \frac{r}{100} \right)$$

If we take logarithms we have[1]

$$\log A = \log P + n \log R \qquad . \qquad . \quad (3)$$

and this gives us a method alternative to that shown in
section 4 above. It is particularly useful if a table of
amounts of £1 is not available.

[1] For $10^{\log A} = 10^{\log P} \times 10^{n \log R} = 10^{\log P + n \log R}.$

Ex. 9. Find the compound interest on £749 for 8 years at $4\frac{1}{2}\%$.

We have $R = 1 + \dfrac{4\frac{1}{2}}{100} = 1 \cdot 045$, $n = 8$, $P = £749$.

		No.	*Log*
$\therefore$ A = PR^8		1·045	0·0191
= £749 × (1·045)^8		× 8	0·1528
= **£1065.**		749	2·8745
	+		**3·0273**

This answer is an approximation, as only 4-figure tables are used. As before, for accuracy, 7-figure tables are desirable.

Inverse problems on compound interest can readily be solved using logarithms.

Ex. 10. £500 is lent for 3 years, and it is understood that, including interest, £600 is to be repaid at the end of that time. What percentage compound interest does this represent, correct to 1 decimal place?

Here we have A = £600, P = £500, $n = 3$.

		No.	*Log*
$\therefore$	$600 = 500\, R^3$		
	so $R^3 = \frac{6}{5}$, i.e. $R = \sqrt[3]{1 \cdot 2}$	1·2	0·0792
$\therefore$	$R = 1 \cdot 063$	÷ 3	0·0264

i.e. $1 + \dfrac{r}{100} = 1 + \cdot 063$

$\therefore$ $r = \mathbf{6 \cdot 3}$

i.e. **percentage interest is 6·3.**

6. Repayment of Loans by Instalments

A common method of repayment of a loan is by instalments once a year. In such a case, for each year the interest on the outstanding principal is added, and the amount of the annual repayment is then subtracted. An example will make this clear.

Ex. 11. Brown buys a car for £850 and borrows the money at 5% per annum compound interest. He agrees to make annual repayments of £200, the first to be paid twelve months after the loan is issued. How much does he still owe immediately after making the third repayment?

1st-year principal	850
Add 5% interest	42·5
	892·5
Less repayment	200
2nd-year principal	692·5
Add 5% interest	34·625
	727·125
Less repayment	200
3rd-year principal	527·125
Add 5% interest	26·35625
	553·48125
Less repayment	200
Outstanding debt	**353·48125**

The amount still owing at that date
= £353·48125
= **£353 9s. 8d.**

$$353·48125$$
$$9·6250$$
$$\overline{7·500}$$

EXERCISE 3

Using the Compound Interest Table in section 4 above, find to the nearest 1d.:

1. The amount of £580 for 4 years at 3%.

2. The amount of £1200 for 10 years at 5%

3. The amount of £685 for 20 years at 2½%.

4. The interest on £2800 for 5 years at 4%.

Using logarithms, find as accurately as you can:

5. The amount of £820 for 6 years at 4½%.

6. The amount of £2040 for 11 years at 3%.

7. The compound interest on £722 for 8 years at 2½%.

8. The compound interest on £28,000 for 6 years at 4%.

9. At what rate per cent., to the nearest 0·1%, is interest charged if a repayment of £750 is to be made at the end of 5 years for a loan of £600?

10. In how many years would a sum of money double itself if invested at 4% compound interest?

11. The compound interest paid on £400 loaned for two years exceeds the simple interest on the same amount for the same time at the same rate per cent., by £1. Find the rate per cent. per annum.

CHAPTER FIFTEEN

RATES, TAXES AND INSURANCE

1. Rates and Taxes

It is not within the scope of this book to give a detailed account of national expenditure or that of local government, but as the costs entailed are borne by the public, everyone should understand the arithmetic involved.

Rates are paid to local authorities, such as Borough or Urban District Councils, for public services. Some of these services are provided by the local council, others are controlled by the County Council, who receive a proportion of the rates paid to the local council. For example, an Urban District Council will deal with housing, parks and cemeteries and public libraries. A County Council will deal with education and fire service, but consultation between the two authorities is necessary for many items.

National expenditure is largely met by the payment of *taxes*. These take many forms including income tax, purchase tax, property tax (known as Schedule A tax), and profits tax. The joint effect of income tax and purchase tax is so heavy that frequently, if not usually, they will exceed 50% of the actual *cost* of the article purchased.

2. Rates

All property, such as houses, shops, factories and business premises in an area are *assessed*. Each property is given an *assessment* or *rateable value*. The calculation of the assessment is rather involved and depends to some extent on a hypothetical net income which could be received if the property were let. Contributory factors in assessing the rateable value of a house are its locality, floor area, size of garden, whether or not there is a garage, and so on. Once the assessment has been made (for an ordinary house the figure might well be £48) it will remain constant for a number of years. The *rates* paid, however, do not. They will vary from year to year and they depend on the annual expenditure of the local authorities. In this connection a simple proportion sum is involved.

Suppose a Borough Council wishes to raise £750,000 in 1957 to cover its expenses, and let us assume that the rateable value of the Borough is £1,000,000. Then the rate levied is $\frac{750,000}{1,000,000}$ of the rateable value, i.e. out of each £1 of rateable value, the council needs

$$£\frac{750,000}{1,000,000} = 15s.$$

We say that **a rate of 15s. in the £** is levied.

Taking our house, mentioned above, as having a rateable value of £48, the actual amount (rate) to be paid is $48 \times 15s. = $ **£36.**

Actual calculations do not work out as conveniently as this example and they are made using decimals of a penny, as will be seen from the extracts from the Rate Demand Note of the Chislehurst and Sidcup U.D.C. for 1957:

Services Administered by the Urban District Council

	s.	d.
Highways and Bridges . . .	0	11·03
House Refuse Removal . . .	0	7·15
etc.		

Services Administered by the County Council

Education	6	0·94
Public Health		10·12
etc.		

Services Administered by Precepting Authorities other than the County Council

| West Kent Main Sewerage Board . | 0 | 4·55 |

Metropolitan Police   .   .   .   I   5·25
  .   etc.   .   .   .   .   .   .
                                                    ─────────
Rate in pound payable by ratepayer   **16   8**

Ex. 1. The total rateable value of a Borough is £1,263,000. The estimated expenditure for 1957 is £877,000. Find the rate in the £ to be levied, to the nearest 1d.

$$\text{Rate to be levied} = \frac{877000}{1263000} \times 20 \text{ s.}$$
$$= \textbf{13s. 11d.} \text{ (to the nearest 1d.)}$$
i.e. the rate will be 13s. 11d. in the £.

Ex. 2. The public lighting in a certain district of rateable value £2,370,000 required a levy of 7·80d. in the £. How much money was needed?

$$\text{Amount required} = 2{,}370{,}000 \times 7{\cdot}80\text{d.}$$
$$= \textbf{£77,025.}$$

EXERCISE I

1. The rate charged is 17s. 2d. in the £. How much will Brown have to pay if his house has a rateable value of £56?

2. If the rateable value of a district is £1,500,000 the rate charged is 16s. 3d. in the £. If the rateable value is increased to £2,000,000 in the same district, what rate in the £ will give the same income to the council?

3. What rate in the £ is charged if £1,723,000 is required by a Borough in which the rateable value is £2,115,000? (Give the answer to 0·01d.)

4. The rateable value of an urban district is £1,864,000. How much will a levy of 1d. in the £ raise?

3. Water Rate

The charge for water rate on a property is normally assessed as a percentage of the Net Annual Value. We shall take the Net Annual Value (N.A.V.) as being the same as the Rateable Value. There is as a rule little difference, if any.

In the Metropolitan Water Board's assessment for 1957, the charge made on each property was 7% of the N.A.V.

Ex. 3. What is the amount payable for water rate on a shop, whose N.A.V. is £250, if the rate is levied at 7% per annum?

$$\text{Charge} = £\tfrac{7}{100} \times 250 = \textbf{£17 10s.}$$

4. Income Tax

Income Tax is the largest single source of revenue for the Exchequer. In the year 1951–2 for example, out of a total revenue of £4,236,000,000 income tax provided £1,753,000,000. This was 8s. 3d. in every £ of revenue.

Income Tax (together with Surtax), Death Duties, Profits Tax, Stamp Duties and Motor Tax are the main forms of direct taxation, while Purchase Tax, Alcohol and Tobacco Taxes, Entertainment Tax, and Customs and Excise Duties constitute the main body of indirect taxes.

Everyone who has a source of income must declare it to his local Inspector of Taxes, so that the tax to be paid on his income can be calculated. The calculation of Income Tax varies almost every year, so examples must perforce be based on the figures used in 1957, the current year. Although the numbers involved are subject to substantial variation, the method can be applied at any time, and is best illustrated by a fairly comprehensive example.

Ex. 4. A married man with two children earns £1550 in 1957. He pays a superannuation contribution of 5% of his salary. Earned-income allowance is two-ninths of net salary. His personal allowance as a married man is £240 and the allowance for each child is £100. The first £60 of taxable income is charged at 2s. 3d. in the £, the next £150 at 4s. 9d., and the next £150 at 6s. 9d. The balance, if any, is taxed at the Standard Rate of 8s. 6d. in the £. He has an endowment assurance policy on which the premium is £75 per annum. Family Allowance of 8s. a week is payable to the man with two children. He owns a house, of which the N.A.V. is £48. Calculate the Income Tax due.

	£	£
EMPLOYMENT etc. . . .		1550
less Expenses	—	
Superannuation (5%) . .	77	
National Insurance Contributions . . .	11	88
		1462
less ALLOWANCES		
Earned-Income Allowance ($\frac{2}{9}$ths)	325	
Personal Allowance (married man)	240	
Wife's Earned-Income Allowance	—	
Housekeeper . . .	—	
Children	200	
Dependent Relatives . .	—	
Life Insurance ($\frac{2}{5}$ of premium allowed)	30	
Building Society Interest .	—	
TOTAL ALLOWANCES . .	795	
less Family Allowance . .	16	
	779	779
Net Amount chargeable to tax		683

	£	s.	d.
Tax at 2s. 3d. in the £ on £60 .	6	15	0
Tax at 4s. 9d. in the £ on £150 .	35	12	6
Tax at 6s. 9d. in the £ on £150 .	50	12	6
Tax at 8s. 6d. in the £ on £323 .	137	5	6
TAX ASSESSED FOR 1955–57 **£**	**230**	**5**	**6**

The above example is laid out in a manner similar to that of Form P70C (1955–56). Some items on the original have been omitted as they are easily understood, and they are not necessary for the calculation required in this problem. This form is sent to all salary- or wage-earners each year and it is extremely important that it should be clearly understood by everyone.

One or two points in the above calculation require elucidation. The National Insurance Contribution of £11 is not specified in the question, but is the amount likely to have been charged for this assessment. The Family Allowance of £16 is added in as though earned income. It is arrived at as follows:

$$52 \times 8s. = 416s.$$
$$less \ \tfrac{2}{9}\text{ths of this} \quad \underline{92s.}$$
$$\mathbf{324s. = £16\ 4s.}$$

∴ £16, to the nearest £, is entered where shown.

The Earned-Income Allowance of £325 is $\tfrac{2}{9} \times £1462$, i.e. it is based on *net* earnings

On the actual form P70C there is space for adjustment of tax from previous years. This can easily be checked in practice by comparison with previous years' assessments. These notices should be kept permanently, as it is by no means unusual for tax adjustments to be made for income received several years earlier.

So far no mention of the man's house has been made. This is because all the above calculations are charged to earned income, *Schedule E*. A separate account is kept for house property, and it is known as *Schedule A*.

The Annual Value of property assessed under Schedule A is subject to certain deductions (in particular an allowance for repairs, given in the table below). The net figure then obtained is called the Net Annual Value (N.A.V.).

Repairs Allowance (extract from Schedule A Demand Note).

Annual Value	Allowance
Not exceeding £40	One-fourth of Annual Value
Exceeding £40 but not exceeding £50	£10
Exceeding £50 but not exceeding £100	One-fifth of Annual Value
Exceeding £100	£20 + one-sixth of amount by which Annual Value exceeds £100

Thus, in the example being considered:

Annual Value	£60	
less $\frac{1}{5}$ of this	12	
N.A.V.	£48	as given

The Schedule A Demand Note would thus read as follows:

Parish Key and Assessment Nos.	Amount Chargeable			Tax Payable		
		£	s.	£	s.	d.
	at 2s. 3d. in the £					
	at 4s. 9d. in the £					
	at 6s. 9d. in the £					
	at 8s. 6d. in the £	48	—	20	8	0
less allowance of tax, if any				—	—	—
AMOUNT PAYABLE on or before 1st Jany. 1957				20	8	0

The entry under amount chargeable is the N.A.V., and tax on this at 8s. 6d. is £20 8s. The tax is charged at the standard rate because all the reduced rates have been used up in making the assessment for the man under Schedule E. Had his income been considerably smaller, so that he did not pay any tax at 8s. 6d. in the £, then he would have had reduced rates allowed on the Schedule A assessment as well.

Finally, then, we have the total Income Tax he has to pay:

Schedule E	£230	5	6
Schedule A	£ 20	8	0
Total	**£250**	**13**	**6**

Deduction of Income Tax from unearned income, such as investments in Government securities and stocks and shares, is illustrated in the next chapter. There is virtually no difference, except that the two-ninths earned-income relief is not allowable, in general.

5. Insurance

Insurance in modern times is a complicated matter, and this section can only serve as a brief introduction to the subject. An excellent comprehensive treatment is given in Mr. Cockerell's book, "Teach Yourself Insurance", a companion volume to this book.

Briefly, insurance can be classified into two sections:

(a) Life Assurance
(b) Property Insurance.

(a) Life Assurance

The following table shows the division of this section.

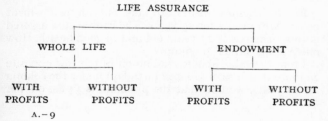

A *whole life* policy is one in which the assured person cannot himself benefit. His dependents receive a sum of money in the event of his death.

An *endowment* policy is one taken out for a specified number of years (say 10, 15, 20, 25 or 30 years). If the policy-holder survives the date of maturity of the policy he can himself receive the sum assured. If he should die before this time his dependents will receive the money at the time of his death.

A *with-profits* policy shares in the profits of the company, and every fifth year (or quinquennium) a bonus is declared and is added to the capital sum assured. On the other hand, a *without-profits* policy does not participate in this way. The sum assured remains constant.

The following table for "Endowment Assurances— With Profits" will illustrate the principles. The sum assured is payable at the end of the period of years specified or at previous death.

ANNUAL PREMIUM FOR EACH £100 ASSURED

Age Next Birthday	Number of Years														
	10			15			20			25			30		
	£	s.	d.	£	s.	d.	£	s.	d.	£	s.	d.	£	s.	d.
26	10	18	9	7	6	10	5	10	2	4	8	5	3	13	8
27	10	18	10	7	6	11	5	10	3	4	8	7	3	13	10
28	10	18	10	7	7	0	5	10	4	4	8	9	3	14	1
29	10	18	10	7	7	1	5	10	6	4	8	11	3	14	4

(This table is subject to modification from time to time. The figures quoted were valid in March 1957.)

Ex. 5. Thomas wishes to take out an endowment policy with profits for 25 years. The capital sum assured is £800. Thomas is 27 years old and in good health. How much is his annual premium?

From the table above, reading off in the row opposite 28 (note that it says age *next* birthday) under the column for 25 years, we find that the premium is £4 8s. 9d. per £100.

∴ Annual premium to be paid = £4 8s. 9d. × 8
= **£35 10s. 0d.**

It is worth bearing in mind that the actual cost each year is appreciably less. If Thomas pays Income Tax, the net cost would be obtained after allowing for a scale of tax relief allowance.

In general, and with certain limitations, premiums paid for life assurance are subject to Income-Tax relief at the appropriate rate on (a) the amount of the premiums paid in the year of assessment, if less than £10, (b) £10, if the premiums paid are between £10 and £25, (c) two-fifths of the premiums paid, if more than £25.

Thus, Thomas' net outgoing for his Life Assurance, assuming his income entitles him to relief at 8s. 6d. in the £, would be

Annual premium £35 10 0
less ⅖ of £35 10s. at 8s. 6d. in the £ . . 6 0 8

Net outgoing £29 9 4

[The £6 0s. 8d. is obtained as follows:

⅖ of £35 10s. = £14 4s. = 284s.

Tax relief = $\frac{8\frac{1}{2}}{20}$ × 284s. = 120·7s. = £6 0s. 8d. (to nearest 1d.).]

Thomas would pay the full premium of £35 10s. to the company and the relief of £6 0s. 8d. would be allowed in his Income Tax Assessment.

A comparison of premiums is interesting for, say, present age 27 years.

1. Endowment with profits (25 years) £4 8s. 9d. ⎫
2. Endowment without profits (25 years) £3 7s. 5d. ⎬ per
3. Whole life with profits £2 8s. 5d.[1] ⎭ £100
4. Whole life without profits £1 12s. 4d.[1]

[1] Premiums payable for life.

There is a big difference in premium for each class of assurance, but there is also a big difference in cover. There is little doubt that, if the higher cost can be met, then endowment assurance with profits is by far the best for most purposes.

(b) Property Insurance

The most important forms of insurance for the average man are:

$\begin{cases}$ (1) House insurance (if owner of the house); $\\$ (2) Contents insurance; $\end{cases}$
    (3) Car insurance.

These are normally effected on separate policies. The premiums for (1) and (2) above are small. Those for (3) are not. The size of a premium clearly depends on the number of claims made each year, and those made for theft of property or fire are few compared with the enormous number of claims made for motor traffic accidents.

House insurance is best effected at a rate of 2s. 3d. per £100 insured. Contents can be insured for 5s. per £100. There are cheaper rates, but for the few pence involved far greater protection is given by utilising these two figures.

Ex. 6. Harris bought a house worth £3,200 and valued the contents at £1,400. How much a year would his premium be for both, if the house was insured at 2s. 3d. per £100 and the contents at 5s. per £100?

Premium for house 2s. 3d. × 32   = £3 12 0
Premium for contents 5s. × 14   = £3 10 0
Annual premium altogether   **£7   2 0**

It is sad, but Income Tax rebate can be claimed for few forms of insurance other than life (including endowment policies), superannuation or pension insurance. Thus, no relief can be claimed for Harris' premium.[1]

[1] It is possible to include insurance of house, *not* contents, in making maintenance claims. For calculation of such claims see "Key to Income Tax and Surtax", edited by Ronald Staples, Taxation Publishing Co., Ltd., W.1.

The calculations for car insurance are different for almost every car and driver, so no attempt will be made to deal with them here. It is best to get quotations from different companies as there are appreciable variations in vehicle insurance, but it should be borne carefully in mind that the cheapest forms of insurance are very far from being the best. For the owner of a car, a comprehensive policy with a good insurance company or with Lloyd's is a valuable safeguard.

EXERCISE 2

Lay out the following in the form of the example on Income Tax given in section 4 above. Take the rates of tax as the same, but ignore National Insurance contribution.

1. A single man earns £800 per annum in 1957. He pays 6% superannuation contribution. His personal allowance as a single man is £140. Find how much tax he pays.

2. A man earning £1084 per annum has a wife and one child. He does not pay superannuation, but has a life insurance policy on which the premium is £60 per annum. Find the Income Tax paid.

3. A married man with three children earns £1400 per annum. He pays 5% superannuation per annum, and family allowance is 8s. a week for the second and each subsequent child. He has an endowment policy on which the annual premium is £20. Calculate the tax due. He owns his house and the Annual Value is £50. Calculate the N.A.V. and the tax he must pay under Schedule A.

4. Brown is 28 years old and wishes to take out a with-profits policy to mature in 20 years time. How much is the annual premium if the policy is for £600? If tax relief is allowed in accordance with section 5 above, what is the *actual* amount it costs him each year? It is to be assumed that Brown is liable for tax at the standard rate.

CHAPTER SIXTEEN

INVESTMENTS AND THE STOCK EXCHANGE

1. What are Stocks and Shares?

Stocks and shares are holdings, i.e. units of part ownership, in a company or organisation. Anyone who buys such investments becomes a part-owner of the concern, no matter how few shares he may purchase. It does not necessarily follow that he has a say in the running of the business.

In the case of public companies, shareholders are usually invited to attend at Annual General Meetings, where they may have an opportunity of expressing ideas, and where they may vote. The power of their vote is normally proportional to the number of shares held. Shareholders are also able to elect directors or to remove them from office.

The issue of *shares* in companies is normally a permanent matter. So long as the company exists, the shares continue in being. There are certain *loans* raised in developing new premises or activities which are of a temporary nature. They may take the form of *mortgage debentures* on the property of companies or be issued in the form of *redeemable preference shares* (*q.v.*). Loan notes are also sometimes used.

Government loans and those made to local Public Boards are not quite the same. They are normally of two kinds:

(1) A loan may be for a specific period, by the end of which time it will have been redeemed. For example 3% War Stock (1955–59) *could* have been redeemed[1] as early as 1955, but *must* have been redeemed by 1959.

[1] A stock is redeemed by an issuing authority when the holders are paid cash for their stock. The loan then ceases.

(2) The loan may be for an indefinite period, e.g. 4% Consolidated Stock (called Consols for short) is dated *in or after* 1957. This means that the issuing authority, in this case the Government, *can* redeem the stock at any time in 1957 or later, or need not do so at all. So long as the stock is held, interest is paid at 4% per annum.

2. The Stock Exchange

The Stock Exchange, formerly a private institution, but now an important public body, is where the purchase and sale of stocks and shares is carried out. It is a central organisation in which a seller wishing to dispose of a security can be introduced quickly and easily to a buyer. The business is transacted through members of the Stock Exchange. Members of the public cannot themselves enter the Exchange to do business.

Suppose Jones wishes to sell 200 Ordinary Shares of the Ford Motor Company. He telephones or visits his broker (or he may instruct his bank to contact a broker) and tells him to sell the security. If he knows the market value he may also state a minimum price, say 38s.,[1] which he wishes to obtain. His *stockbroker*, in his daily visit to the Stock Exchange, contacts a *stockjobber* who is willing to take the shares on his book at an agreed figure. To get the highest price for his client a broker may contact several jobbers before he is satisfied that he has done as well as possible. Jobber No. 1 may quote 38s. 6d.—39s. 6d., meaning that he will *give* 38s. 6d. for Fords but *charges* 39s. 6d. for them. Jobber No. 2 may quote 38s. 9d.—39s. 7½d. Thus, Jones' broker would get a better price from Jobber No. 2, and, as this would be 9d. more than Jones' minimum figure, a deal might well be made. The jobber does not keep the 200 shares. He waits until another broker comes to him from another client, say Brown, who wishes to buy Fords, and if jobber and broker agree the price, the shares are bought by the broker on behalf of Brown.

[1] For each share.

It will be noticed that a stockjobber is mentioned above. He does not deal directly with the public. He is a man of considerable financial means who holds large quantities of stocks and shares between transactions.

The full story[1] of Jones' sale would read as follows

JONES → BROKER A → JOBBER → BROKER B → BROWN

The broker charges a small commission on each share for his work on behalf of his client. The jobber makes his income on the difference in price between buying and selling, e.g. the jobber who quoted 38s. 9d.—39s. 7½d. would make a profit of 10½d. on each share if he obtained the price asked. On 200 shares this may seem a lot, considering the number of transactions he will carry out in one day, but it should be borne in mind that he holds large quantities of securities on his hands at any one time, and should some of them fall in value during the day, a very frequent event, he may stand to lose substantial sums of money from time to time.

The broker does not hold the stock himself, but acts as surety for his client. Should a client default, the broker may have to meet financial expenses. For this reason, the broker takes care to check the *bona fides* of his clientele.

3. Stocks and Shares

The term "stock" is usually restricted to official issues such as Government Securities, for example 3½% War Loan. The price quoted in *The Times* and in the financial columns of many other newspapers would be found to read, say 69½–70½. The difference represents the range of values within which business is done on a particular day. The average price would be 70 in such a case, and it means that £100 *Stock* (i.e. stock of the *nominal value*[2] of £100) would cost about £70 in money on that day. The £100 stock is *not* worth £100 in cash, although it

[1] See paragraph 7 for the documents involved.
[2] Definitions are given in Para. 4, p. 193. The nominal value is that written on the stock or share certificate.

may have been issued at that price many years ago. The *market value*[1], £70, is determined by the income provided, calculated as a percentage of the cash outlay. When a high percentage return is expected, such as during inflation, the market price falls, and vice versa.

When a company is formed, people are asked to subscribe towards it by taking "shares". The shares are usually for small amounts, such as £1, 10s., 5s., 2s. or 1s., although shares can be found in many shapes and sizes. The shares are rarely worth the same as their nominal value. As with stocks, the price depends on the *yield*, that is, the percentage return.

Consider, again, the purchase of £100 of $3\frac{1}{2}$% War Loan at 70. The cost is £70, but the *dividend* of $3\frac{1}{2}$% is based on the nominal value of the certificate, which is 100, so we have

COST	CERTIFICATE	INCOME
£70 CASH $\longrightarrow$	£100 of $3\frac{1}{2}$% War Loan	$\longrightarrow$ £3 10s. per annum

The yield, expressed as a percentage of outlay, is much more than $3\frac{1}{2}$%, for £70 brings an annual interest of £$3\frac{1}{2}$.

$$\therefore \text{ Percentage yield} = \frac{3\frac{1}{2}}{70} \times 100 = \mathbf{5}.$$

4. Definitions of certain terms used in Stock Exchange procedure

(*a*) The *nominal value* of a security is the amount of stock or shares held. It is written on the stock or share certificate. It does *not* vary from day to day.

(*b*) The *market value* of a security is the value, in money, of the holding, and this may fluctuate from day to day.

(*c*) A *quotation* is the price to be paid for a share or unit of stock. This also varies. Note that: market value = quotation × number of shares.

[1] Definitions are given in Para. 4.

(*d*) A stock is said to stand:

(1) *at par* if it is quoted at its nominal value exactly, e.g. £100 Stock standing at £100 cash, i.e. quoted at 100.

(2) *at a premium* if it is quoted above par, e.g. a £1 share quoted at 25s. stands at a premium of 5s.

(3) *at a discount* if it is quoted below par, e.g. Consols 2½% standing at 59 would stand at a discount of 41. It would cost £59 for £100 Consols.

(*e*) The *dividend* received is the amount of cash paid as interest on a holding. It may be expressed as a percentage of the stock, as in the War Loan above, or it may be given as a sum of money, such as 3d. dividend on each 5s. ordinary share. The latter would be $\frac{3}{60} \times$ 100%, i.e. 5% dividend.

(*f*) The *yield* is the dividend expressed as a percentage of the *cost price*. For example, if the 5s. shares which paid 3d. dividend in (*d*) above cost 6s. 6d. each, the yield would be less than the 5% dividend. It would be

$$\frac{5s.}{6\frac{1}{2}s.} \times 5, \text{ i.e. } 3\frac{11}{13}\%.$$

5. Methods of Calculation

The calculations involved in the purchase and sale of stock are best illustrated by some examples. Those in the first group below will avoid the complications of brokerage and stamp duty, but later some explanation of these expenses is given.

Ex. 1. Find how much 3½% War Stock at 80 can be bought for £500. Calculate also the annual income.

(The stock stands at a discount so the quantity of stock bought will exceed the cash value)

£80 cash buys £100 stock

∴ Amount of stock bought = £$\frac{100}{80}$ × 500

= **£625 stock**

$$\text{Annual income} = £\frac{3\frac{1}{2}}{100} \times 625$$

$$= £21 \cdot 875$$
$$= \textbf{£21 17s. 6d.}$$

Ex. 2. Smith invested £480 in Woolworth 5s. Ordinary Shares quoted at 60s. The annual dividend paid was 2s. 10d. per share. Find (a) the number of shares bought, (b) the actual income received, (c) the yield per cent. on outlay.

The student will notice that the shares are priced very highly, but the dividend is also high compared with the nominal value of the shares, so that a moderate yield is to be anticipated.

The number of shares purchased is quite independent of their nominal value. They cost £3 each.

$$\therefore \text{ Number of shares purchased} = \frac{480}{3}$$
$$= \textbf{160}$$

(Their total *nominal value* is only 160 × 5s. = £40.)

The dividend received is 2s. 10d. per share
i.e. altogether it is 2s. 10d. × 160
$$= \textbf{£22 13s. 4d.}$$

and this is the annual income.

The yield per cent. on outlay

$$= \frac{£22\frac{2}{3}}{£480} \times 100$$

$$= \frac{68 \times 100}{3 \times 480}\% = 4\frac{13}{18}\%.$$

This example is interesting in that it illustrates the flaw in certain popular fallacies concerning dividends. There are many who believe that the payment by a company of 50% dividend implies enormous profits to the shareholders. This is not so, for the above example shows that whereas the dividend of 2s. 10d. per 5s. share actually exceeds 50%, the yield on capital gained by a shareholder is only $4\frac{13}{18}\%$, less than he would get if he bought National Savings Certificates, when account is taken of Income Tax.

A company pays dividends in accordance with its profits. The company may grow enormously over many years of carefully handled business, and may employ more and more people and have greatly increased premises. It does not usually increase its share capital (i.e. the number of shares issued) to anything like the same extent, so the value of the individual shares will rise. They frequently change hands, so that shareholders are unlikely to get greatly increased dividends as a whole. The percentage interest received depends on *yield* based on the cost of the share, i.e. the market value, not on the dividend, which is based on the nominal value.

Ex. 3. Thompson invested £640 in Qualcast 5s. shares paying 24% dividend. He received an income of £36. At what price did the shares stand when he bought them?

The dividend from one share $= \frac{24}{100} \times 5s.$

$$= £\frac{24}{100} \times \frac{5}{20} = £\frac{3}{50}$$

∴ If x is the number of shares, the yield is $£\frac{3}{50}x$, but we know that this is £36

$$\therefore \frac{3}{50}x = 36$$

$$\text{so } 3x = 36 \times 50$$

$$\therefore x = \frac{36 \times 50}{3} = 600 \text{ shares.}$$

∴ 600 shares cost £640

so 1 share costs $£\frac{640}{600}$

i.e. $\frac{640 \times 20}{600}$ shillings $= \frac{64}{3}s. = 21\frac{1}{3}s.$

that is, **these shares stand at 21s. 4d.**

Ex. 4. Messrs. Atkinson & Wright Ltd. hold £10,000 $2\frac{1}{2}$% Savings Bonds. They sell their investment at 77 and reinvest the proceeds in British Electricity $4\frac{1}{2}\%$ Stock (1967–69) at 90. Find the change in the annual income.

This type of problem should be divided mentally into stages.

(1) *Original Income* $= \dfrac{2\frac{1}{2}}{100} \times £10,000 = $ **£250**

(2) Amount of money realised on sale

$$= £10,000 \times \tfrac{77}{100}$$

(3) Amount of stock purchased $= \tfrac{100}{90} \times$ sum invested

$$= £10,000 \times \tfrac{77}{100} \times \tfrac{100}{90}$$

(4) *New income* $= \dfrac{4\frac{1}{2}}{100} \times$ amount of *new* stock held

$$= £10,000 \times \frac{77}{100} \times \frac{100}{90} \times \frac{4\frac{1}{2}}{100}$$

$$= \textbf{£385.}$$

∴ There is an increase in income of
$$£(385 - 250) = \textbf{£135.}$$

EXERCISE I

1. Find how much 3% War Stock quoted at 88 can be bought for £1100. Also find the annual interest received.

2. Brown invests £400 in $2\frac{1}{2}\%$ Consols at 60. What is the yield per cent. and what is his annual income?

3. Which gives the higher yield: (*a*) $3\frac{1}{2}\%$ War Stock at 77 *or* (*b*) 4% Victory Bonds at 94? (Assume that £100 had been invested in each security, and compare the results.)

4. What is the cost of 250 Brand 4s. shares at 7s. 3d. each? If they pay 20% dividend, what is the annual income from them?

5. What is the yield per cent. if Bryant & May 14% Preference Shares of £1 cost 40s. 6d. each? (Give the answer in £ s. d.%.)

6. Jones bought 180 Ranks 5s. shares for £210. At what price were they quoted?

7. Smith holds 340 Raleigh £1 shares and receives an income of £42 10s. from them. What is the rate per cent. dividend?

8. Robinson sells £640 British Electricity $4\frac{1}{4}$% stock at 85. How much does he receive? He reinvests the money in $3\frac{1}{2}$% Funding Stock at 75. Find by how much his annual income changes.

9. Williams sells 615 Lancashire Cotton £1 shares at 24s. 6d. How many British Celanese £1 shares can he buy at 15s. 3d. with the proceeds of the sale?

10. Briggs invested £286 in British Home Stores 1s. shares at 5s. 6d. How many shares did he get? He sold them when the price had risen to 6s. 3d. How much did he make on the sale?

6. Expenses Involved in the Purchase and Sale of Securities

There are three items of expenditure involved in buying and selling stocks and shares, other than the actual cost of the securities. These incidental expenses usually total about 4% of the price of the shares, and are as follows:

(1) Stamp Duty (i.e. cost of Transfer Stamp)
(2) Brokerage
(3) Contract Stamp.

Of these, the Contract Stamp charge is very small and can be neglected when working problems in this book, if desired.

6a. Stamp Duty

This is a duty payable to the Government when a transfer of stock (or shares) is made. For many years the charge was 1% of the amount of money involved in the transaction. Since the 1939–45 War, the charge has been increased to 2%. It is calculated as follows:

TRANSFER STAMPS

Cost of Security, not exceeding (£'s)	Duty Payable £ s. d.		
5	0	2	0
10	0	4	0
15	0	6	0
20	0	8	0
25	0	10	0
50	1	0	0
75	1	10	0
100	2	0	0
125	2	10	0
150	3	0	0
175	3	10	0
200	4	0	0
225	4	10	0
250	5	0	0
275	5	10	0
300	6	0	0
350	7	0	0
400	8	0	0

NOTE

British Funds (e.g. Consols and War Loan) and many Public Corporation Stocks are free of Stamp Duty.

and so on at the rate of 20s. for every further £50 or fractional part thereof.

It will be observed that the Transfer Stamp normally costs more than 2% of the amount spent on the security. This expense is borne by the buyer, not by the seller (except in the case of very small transactions, when alternative arrangements are sometimes made).

6b. Brokerage

A full table of the scale of minimum commissions payable to stockbrokers would be much too long for inclusion in a book of this type. Stockbrokers have an accepted scale of payments and a few examples are given

below. The full list is easily obtained, if required, from
any stockbroking firm or from a bank.

SCALE OF MINIMUM COMMISSIONS

Government Securities etc.
$\left\{\begin{array}{l}\frac{3}{8}\% \text{ up to } £10,000 \\ \frac{1}{4}\% \text{ on any balance} \\ \quad \text{in excess of this} \\ \quad \text{amount}\end{array}\right.$

Shares or Units of Stock

Price 1s. or under	.	.	at discretion
1s.–1s. 6d.	.	.	$\frac{1}{4}$d.
1s. 6d.–2s. 6d.	.	.	$\frac{1}{2}$d.
2s. 6d.–3s. 6d.	.	.	$\frac{3}{4}$d.
3s. 6d.–5s.	.	.	1d.
5s.–10s.	.	.	$1\frac{1}{2}$d.
10s.–15s.	.	.	$2\frac{1}{4}$d.
15s.–£1	.	.	3d.
£1–£1 10s.	.	.	$3\frac{3}{4}$d.
£1 10s.–£2	.	.	$4\frac{1}{2}$d.
£2–£2 10s.	.	.	6d. etc.

The *brokerage is based on the market value of a share*,
not on its nominal value. For example, the brokerage on
a 5s. share costing 35s. 6d. would be $4\frac{1}{2}$d.

Brokerage is paid by the buyer to his own broker and
also by the seller to *his* broker. When an investor reinvests the proceeds of the sale of a security at once, a
broker normally charges a reduced commission on the
amount of money reinvested (say, half the above scale).

6c. Contract Stamp

This is a stamp which must be affixed (by law) to a
Contract Note. The procedure will be explained in
paragraph 7 below.

Where the value of the shares or stock marketed costs:

From			
£5– £100	1 shilling		
£100– £500	2 shillings		
£500–£1000	4 shillings	CONTRACT
£1000–£1500	6 shillings	STAMP
£1500–£2500	8 shillings	
£2500–£5000	12 shillings etc.	

7. Documents Involved in the Purchase of Securities

If we refer back to paragraph 2 above we see that Jones' broker has sold his shares at 38s. 9d. The broker will now immediately send Jones a *Contract Note* made out as follows:

CONTRACT NOTE 1

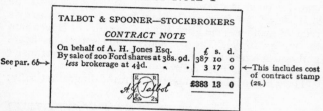

See par. 6b→	TALBOT & SPOONER—STOCKBROKERS			
	CONTRACT NOTE			
	On behalf of A. H. Jones Esq.	£	s.	d.
	By sale of 200 Ford shares at 38s. 9d.	387	10	0
	less brokerage at 4¾d.	3	17	0
	A. Talbot	**£383 13 0**		←This includes cost of contract stamp (2s.)

This is a guarantee to the seller that Talbot & Spooner will send the sum of £383 13s. in due course when the transfer is completed.

In the meantime the shares have passed through the hands of the jobber to broker B (of the firm of Hart & Field, say), who buys them on behalf of Brown at a price of, perhaps, 39s. 7½d. Hart & Field send a contract note to Brown made out as follows:

CONTRACT NOTE 2

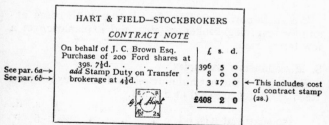

	HART & FIELD—STOCKBROKERS			
	CONTRACT NOTE			
	On behalf of J. C. Brown Esq.	£	s.	d.
	Purchase of 200 Ford shares at 39s. 7¼d.	396	5	0
See par. 6a→	*add* Stamp Duty on Transfer	8	0	0
See par. 6b→	brokerage at 4¾d.	3	17	0
	G. L. Hart	**£408 2 0**		←This includes cost of contract stamp (2s.)

Now this is sent to Brown, who holds it until the transfer is completed. As soon as Brown receives this contract note he sends £408 2s. to Hart & Field. Jones will have sent his share certificate (proof that he had two hundred

Ford Shares for sale) to Talbot & Spooner. The brokers now complete a *Transfer Deed* which has to be signed by Jones, in the presence of a witness, as seller, and by Brown, in the presence of a witness, as buyer. It is to this transfer deed that the costly transfer stamp is affixed (£8 in the example under discussion). When the transfer deed is completed it is sent, together with the share certificate formerly held by Jones, to the company's registered offices (the Ford Motor Company of Dagenham in our example). The company cancels the certificate and issues a new one in the name of Brown. The transfer of the shares is now complete.

The whole of the business is illustrated diagramatically:

We shall now complete the chapter with some examples involving brokerage etc., and explanation of a few terms used.

8. Miscellaneous Examples

Ex. 5. Find the net amount realised when 250 Austin Reed £1 shares are sold at 24s. 6d.

	£	s.	d.
250 shares at 24s. 6d.	306	5	0
Less brokerage at 3¾d. + contract stamp 2s.	4	0	1½
	£302	**4**	**10½**

Ex. 6. What is the total cost of 1000 Walters' Palm Toffee 1s. Deferred Shares at 2s. 3d.?

	£	s.	d.
1000 at 2s. 3d.	112	10	0
Add Brokerage at ½d. . .	2	1	8
Contract stamp . . .	0	2	0
Transfer stamp . . .	2	10	0
	£117	**3**	**8**

Ex. 7. Smithers sells 500 Crittal Manufacturing Co. 5s. shares at 7s. He reinvests the money in Distillers 6s. 8d. shares at 21s. 3d. How many does he get? The broker allows half commission rate on the reinvestment.

	£	s.	d.
500 at 7s.	175	0	0
Less brokerage at 1½d. ⎫ + contract stamp 2s. ⎭ .	3	4	6
Amount realised on sale . .	**£171**	**15**	**6**

The new purchase is probably most easily approached indirectly as follows. The stamp duty on £171 15s. 6d. would be £3 10s., leaving £168 5s. 6d.

The cost of the shares is 21s. 3d. plus half brokerage, 1⅞d. (being ½ of 3¾d.), i.e. 21s. 4⅞d. per share. Now it would be exceedingly tiresome to divide £168 5s. 6d. by 21s. 4⅞d., whereas 21s. 5d. is a practical divisor.

$$21s. 5d. = 257 \text{ pence}$$
$$£168 5s. 6d. = 40386 \text{ pence}$$
$$\therefore \text{Number of shares} = \frac{40386}{257}$$
$$= \mathbf{157.}$$

```
            157
      257)40386
           257
          1468
          1285
          1836
          1799
            37
```

In practice, from a set of tables, the approximate number of shares which could be purchased would be found, say 155 or 160 shares. The cash adjustment necessary would be made after the purchase of these shares. It would only be a few pounds one way or the other.

EXERCISE 2

1. Find the net amount realised on the sale of 400 Brickwoods 6% "A" £1 Cumulative Preference Shares at 19s. 6d.

2. Calculate the total cost of 720 Bryant & May 14% £1 Cumulative Preference Shares at 44s. a share.

3. Find the total cost of 800 English Electric £1 shares at 52s. 6d.

4. Thompson sells 400 Emu Wine "A" 5s. shares at 7s. 6d. and 80 Imperial Chemical £1 shares at 43s. 9d. Find the amount he receives altogether. (Each transaction requires a separate contract note.)

5. Stannard invested £280 in J. Lyons £1 shares at 88s. Find the number of shares bought, and the annual income received if the shares pay an annual dividend of 22½%. What is the yield per cent. on outlay (to 0·1%)? (Brokerage is 1s. per share.)

9. Some Types of Stocks and Shares

The reader will have noticed such names as Preference Shares and Ordinary Shares in this chapter. A short explanation will now be given.

Most of the stocks issued by the Government and by Local Authorities are fixed-interest holdings; that is, they pay a definite dividend each year. These stocks are quoted in units of £100, but they may be bought in units of £1, or even sometimes in units of 1d. For example, a Certificate for £228 17s. 4d. of 3½% War Loan would be quite usual.

Shares in companies are more varied. We shall divide them into two classes: I. Fixed-Interest Holdings; II. Equities.

There are hybrids of I and II as well.

I. *Fixed-Interest Holdings*

(*a*) *Debentures.* These are a mortgage holding on the property of a company.

(*b*) *Preference Shares.* These are, in general, fixed-interest certificates, but their dividend is paid out of profits before the ordinary shareholders are entitled to consideration. There are two *main* types of Preference Share: *Cumulative*—meaning that if the dividend is missed during a period of poor trading it must be made up later; *Non-cumulative*—meaning that if payment is not made in any year, there is no obligation to make it good later. Most preference shares are cumulative.

II. *Equities*

(*a*) *Ordinary Shares.* These are paid out of the profits after all expenses have been met and debenture and preference shareholders satisfied. They can be paid any dividend the directors think suitable, and the dividend frequently varies from year to year, or even more often.

Of other kinds of stock and share, and subdivisions of the above (e.g. Participating Preference Shares, Preferred Ordinary Stock, Prior Lien Debentures) there is not the space to deal.

10. Income Tax

The dividends received from holdings of stocks and shares rank as unearned income, and no earned-income relief is allowable. The tax is deducted at the standard rate on almost all securities, before a cheque for dividend due is sent to a shareholder. Should the shareholder not earn enough to pay tax at the standard rate, he is entitled to claim back the difference between his rate of tax and the standard rate from the taxation authorities when he fills in his annual Income-Tax return.

Ex. 8. Roberts buys 240 £1 General Electric 6½% "A" Cumulative Preference Shares. Find his net annual income after allowing for tax at 8s. 6d. in the £.

$$\text{The gross income} = £240 \times \frac{6\frac{1}{2}}{100}.$$

Now as 8½s. are paid in tax out of 20s., the income is 11½s. net for every 20s. gross.

$$\therefore \text{Net income} = £240 \times \frac{6\frac{1}{2}}{100} \times \frac{11\frac{1}{2}}{20}$$

$$= \frac{\overset{3}{\overset{60}{240}} \times 13 \times 23}{\underset{100}{\underset{2000}{2000}} \times \underset{1}{4}}$$

$$= £8 \cdot 97 = \textbf{£8 19s. 5d.}$$

$$\begin{array}{r} 8 \cdot 97 \\ \hline 19 \cdot 4 \\ \hline 4 \cdot 8 \end{array}$$

EXERCISE 3

1. Find the net income from 2000 Crittall Manufacturing Company £1 5½% First Cumulative Preference Shares, with tax deducted at 9s. in the £1.

2. Ilford 5s. shares pay 15% dividend. Find the income from 600 of these shares, if tax is deducted at the rate of 8s. 6d. in the £.

3. Jenkins holds the following securities:
　　1500 Joshua Hoyle 2s. shares paying 12½%
　　£360 Odeon Properties 4% Debenture Stock
　　£816 3½% War Loan.
Find the net income with tax deducted at 9s. in the £

CHAPTER SEVENTEEN

COMPUTING MACHINES AND THE BINARY SCALE

1. Calculating Machines

Calculating machines have been in existence for a considerable number of years. Simple desk machines were made as early as the eighteen-eighties, but it is only recently that high-speed electronic machines of great efficiency have been devised. To a layman these are still a mystery, and they are indeed of very complex construction. The arithmetic of this chapter will be devoted to a particularly important machine, the *digital computer*, in which the basic operation is counting. Such a machine can perform the operations of addition, subtraction, multiplication and division and many more complex processes. Early digital computers were mechanical but the latest models are almost entirely electrical. Teleprinters are often incorporated in these machines.

In addition to the digital computer there is another type of machine called the *analogue machine*, or continuous operator. This is a mathematical instrument in which there is a *continuous variation* of some physical quantity such as an electrical resistance. This is in sharp contrast to the basis of the digital computer, wherein the steps are of *one unit*, not of continuity. (A very simple example of an analogue machine is the slide rule, in which two lengths, representing two numbers to be multiplied together, are placed end to end and added. As any two numbers will give any two lengths, there is a continuous variation possible.) Analogue machines are often used for solving differential equations[1]: such

---

[1] See "Teach Yourself Calculus": P. Abbott, E.U.P.

machines sometimes being given the name of "differential analysers". Analogue machines are taken to pieces rather like a fantastic Meccano set, and reassembled differently for each different kind of problem. Digital computers, on the other hand, once built need not be modified. A particular programme fed into a digital machine may not require the utilisation of more than a limited part of the total access available. As analogue machines involve mathematics of a complex nature unsuited to a book on simple arithmetic we shall not consider them in further detail.

A digital computer consists of a vast collection of circuits through which electric currents can flow. This flow is regulated by thermionic valves. (Research is being carried out to see whether these valves, which have frequently to be replaced, can be superseded by transistors. Difficulties in utilising transistors are considerable, as their characteristics vary widely when temperature changes are small.) If the impulse received is sufficiently large a current passes through a particular circuit: if not, no current flows in this section of the network. This implies the choice of two, and only two, possibilities —Yes or No.

Now this is the same as counting in the *scale of two* (the binary scale), for the only basic numbers which are permitted are 0 (no current) and 1 (current flowing).

It is therefore clear that, for such a machine to work, it is necessary that a problem to be solved shall be converted into the binary scale, and the answer at the end shall be converted back. Before we actually carry out some calculations in the binary scale, it is worth spending a few moments considering whether the popular name "electronic brains" applied to such machines has in fact any justification.

There is no structural similarity between the nervous system and computing machines, but there is a remarkable resemblance between a direct nervous impulse and the action of a thermionic valve or a relay. In each case there is or is not a result, and the magnitude of this result does not vary. Computing machines calculate as we do, but they are vastly more efficient, for they are very much quicker and far more accurate. The elements of the brain are to some extent independent of one another, so in fact are the circuits of an electronic machine. The machine can store information fed into it and reissue that information as required—this is a kind of memory. There is little likelihood of devising machines of such complexity as the brain, which has some 10^{10} cells, whereas the biggest digital computers only have about 10^4 separate circuits.

2. The Binary Scale

When we use the scale of ten (the *decimal* scale) we count from 0 to 9, but when we reach ten, we put a *one* in the tens column thus, 10, and start again 10, 11 ... 99. When we reach one hundred, which is ten times ten, we put a *one* in the hundreds column thus, 100, and carry on 100, 101, 102. ... As already explained in Chapter 2, the number 5278 is really

$$5 \times 1000 + 2 \times 100 + 7 \times 10 + 8,$$
$$\text{i.e. } 5 \times 10^3 + 2 \times 10^2 + 7 \times 10 + 8.$$

Similarly $2030 = 2 \times 10^3 + 0 \times 10^2 + 3 \times 10 + 0$.

Now the *binary scale* is obtained in exactly the same way. A number is expressed as powers of 2. Consider the number 43 of the ordinary decimal scale. Now
$$43 = 1 \times 2^5 + 0 \times 2^4 + 1 \times 2^3 + 0 \times 2^2 + 1 \times 2 + 1.$$
∴ In the binary scale 43 is 101011, for every time we reach 2 we proceed to the next column (e.g. $3 = 1 \times 2 + 1$, so in the binary scale it becomes 11).

We do not read a number 101011 in the binary scale as "one hundred and one thousand and eleven". As no separate nomenclature has been given to this scale of numbers, we say in words that the number 101011 is "one nought one nought one one".

How then do we calculate these strange new numbers? It is really very simple. We merely divide by 2 repeatedly, thus:

```
2)43
2)21 + 1
2)10 + 1
2) 5 + 0
2) 2 + 1
   1 + 0
```

The answer is read round the edge as **101011**.
Notice the remarkable resemblance to the method of reading off the answer in 15th-century arithmetic in Chapter 1.

The number of digits in a number expressed in the binary scale is about three times as many as that in the decimal scale. This does not imply any difficulty of manipulation. In fact, nothing could be easier than the addition and multiplication tables. They are completely expressed as follows:

Addition Table

$$0 + 0 = 0 \quad \text{(nought)}$$
$$1 + 0 = 1 \quad \text{(one)}$$
$$1 + 1 = 10 \quad \text{(one nought)}$$

Multiplication Table

$$0 \times 0 = 0 \quad \text{(nought)}$$
$$1 \times 0 = 0 \quad \text{(nought)}$$
$$1 \times 1 = 1 \quad \text{(one)}$$

The immediate reaction might well be that there would be a great welcome in primary schools for such a system which would save so much of the grind of simple arithmetic. Perusal of the following examples may lead to a modification of that first impression.

We shall now apply our new system to the "four rules" of arithmetic.

Ex. 1. Add together 17, 6 and 23 in the binary scale.

```
2)17              2)6              2)23
2) 8 + 1          2)3 + 0          2)11 + 1
2) 4 + 0          1 + 1            2) 5 + 1
2) 2 + 0                           2) 2 + 1
   1 + 0                              1 + 0
```

```
      17                    10001
       6                      110
      23                    10111
     ───                   ──────
      46 (decimal)         101110 (binary)
```

Notes (a) In the binary scale $1 + 1 = 0$ and carry 1
     (b) $1 + 1 + 1 = 1$ and carry 1.

To convert back to the decimal scale, when necessary, is merely to reverse the reasoning:

$$101110 = 1 \times 2^5 + 0 \times 2^4 + 1 \times 2^3 + 1 \times 2^2 + 1 \times 2 + 0$$
$$= 32 + 0 + 8 + 4 + 2 + 0$$
$$= 46.$$

Ex. 2. Multiply 23 by 48 in the binary scale.

```
      48 ×                 110000 ×
      23                    10111
     ───                   ──────
     144                   110000
      96                   110000
    ────                   110000
    1104                   000000
                           110000
                          ───────────
                          10001010000
```

Notice that, had we reversed the order of multiplication, much labour could have been saved by filling in the four zeros first:

```
           10111 ×
          110000
         ───────────
        10111 0000
        10111
       ───────────
       10001010000
```

Converting back

$$10001010000 = 2^{10} + 2^6 + 2^4$$
$$= 1024 + 64 + 16$$
$$= 1104.$$

Ex. 3. Multiply 243 by 47 in the binary scale.

This example is given to illustrate the magnitude of the task when large numbers are manipulated. It also points out the method of handling larger carrying figures.

```
    243 ×          |        11110011 ×
     47            |          101111
  _____         |        _____
   1701            |        11110011
    972            |        11110011
  _____         |        11110011
  11421            |        11110011
                   |       11110011 0
                   |      _____
                   |      10110010011101
                   |      1 2 3 3 3 3 2 1 1 1 1
```

Checking back the result:
$$2^{13} = 8192$$
$$2^{11} = 2048$$
$$2^{10} = 1024$$
$$2^{7} = 128$$
$$2^{4} = 16$$
$$2^{3} = 8$$
$$2^{2} = 4$$
$$1 = 1$$

$$\overline{11421}$$

It is now clear why the system, fundamentally so simple, is only really suitable for accurate high-speed calculating machines. The multiplication of two five-figure numbers in the decimal scale is likely to become fifteen rows of fifteen-figure numbers in the binary scale, involving an answer of some thirty digits.

It might be noticed in passing that the carrying figures placed underneath the appropriate columns in the above example are in the decimal notation. We can use this (although it will not be written hereafter in this chapter) if we are careful to divide by 2, thus:

1 + 1 + 1 + 1 + 1 = 1 and carry 2 (i.e. two *ones*) to the next column.

We end, in the last column, with

$$1 + 1 = 0, \text{ and carry } 1$$
$$= 10 \text{ (one-nought)}$$

Ex. 4. Divide 2077 by 31 in the binary scale.

```
              1000011
    11111)10000000111101
          11111
          ─────
              101110
              11111
              ─────
               11111
               11111
               ─────
               .....
```

Converting the answer back to the decimal scale

$$1000011 \equiv 2^6 + 2 + 1 = \mathbf{67.}$$

EXERCISE I

1. Convert the following decimal numbers to binary numbers:

   (a) 14   (b) 34   (c) 205   (d) 1101   (e) 4758.

2. Convert the following binary numbers to decimal numbers:

   (a) 110   (b) 11   (c) 10101   (d) 100110   (e) 11100101.

3. Add together the following numbers after first converting them to the binary scale. Give the answers in (i) binary scale, (ii) decimal scale.

   (a) 6 + 19 + 8   (b) 21 + 43 + 7
   (c) 103 + 68 + 274   (d) 3024 + 953 + 67 + 118.

4. Subtract 214 from 316 in the binary scale, giving the answer in binary form.

5. Add the following binary numbers, and afterwards convert the result to decimal form: 1011, 11001, 100101, 101110.

6. Evaluate the binary number sum

$$1101 - 100111 + 111000.$$

7. Multiply the following numbers after converting them to binary form. Give the answers in (i) binary scale, (ii) decimal scale.
   (a) 23 × 9   (b) 68 × 27   (c) 104 × 35
   (d) 214 × 6 × 7   (e) 109 × 31 × 14.

8. Divide 2173 by 18 in the binary scale. Give the answer in the scale of two, and then convert it to the scale of ten.

9. Divide 11011101 by 10011, both numbers being in the binary scale. Give the result in (i) binary form, (ii) decimal form.

The future of computing machines is a great one. Problems which involve prodigious quantities of arithmetic, involving possibly years of work by a man, can be done by a machine of this kind in a few minutes. It is, however, necessary to programme the work and this may take weeks on occasion. Programming is arranging the work in a form in which it can be fed into the computer, but it is a highly specialised process and is too lengthy for inclusion in this book.

For those who would like to pursue this topic further, two small books are well worth reading: "Minds and Machines", W. Sluckin: Pelican A 308; Oxford University Conference, April 8–18, 1957, Times Publishing Co. Each of the above costs 2s. 6d. at the time of writing.

ANSWERS

CHAPTER 2

1. 43. 2. 42. 3. (a) 370 (b) 2415 (c) 13539.
4. £57, £56, £64, £56, £41, £74; total wages bill £348.

1. (a) 16 (b) 45. 2. (a) 130 (b) 49. 3. 66.
4. (a) + + (b) − + (c) + − (d) − −.

1. (a) 85 (b) 161 (c) 1512 (d) 2354
2. (a) 408 (b) 2502 (c) 31400 (d) 114948
3. (a) 5072 (b) 11856 (c) 38617 (d) 944672
4. 5796 5. 289085.

1. (a) 353 (b) 246 (c) 8069, rem. 1.
2. 3038 shillings 3. 38
4. 2555 5. $43\frac{37}{41}$.

1. (a) 56 (b) 103 (c) 580
2. (a) 226 (b) 1238 (c) 7088 (d) 65124
3. (a) 161 (b) 2067
4. (a) 388 (b) 2127.
5. 1996 6. 3829
7. (a) 1953 (b) 782 (c) 24273 (d) 92117
8. (a) 9976 (b) 22192 (c) 51330 (d) 733824
9. (a) 12 (b) 37 (c) 293 (d) 4178, rem. 5
10. (a) 49 rem. 41 (b) 38 (c) $36\frac{39}{88}$ (d) $151\frac{90}{133}$
11. (a) 77 (b) 23 (c) 38 (d) 17
12. (a) 27 (b) 5
13. 55380 14. 45 years 15. 519 tons
16. 117 rows (including one incomplete row containing 55 cabbages).
17. 2304 18. 8784 (366 days in 1984)

19. £676 (The year is taken as 52 weeks)
20. 63 miles   21. 86400
22. The error is $(1732-1723) \times 27 = 9 \times 27 = 243$
23. (a) 450   (b) 599   (c) 300   24. £138 12s.

CHAPTER 3

EXERCISE I   *page 24*

1. (a) 2   (b) 2, 3, 6   (c) 2, 3, 5, 6   (d) 2, 3, 4, 5, 6   (e) 5
2. (a) Divisible by both   (b) Divisible by both
   (c) Divisible by 9 but not by 8
3. (a) $2 \times 3 \times 3$ (b) $2 \times 2 \times 3 \times 5$
   (c) $2 \times 2 \times 3 \times 7 \times 11$ (d) $3 \times 7 \times 11 \times 13$
4. (a) $2^4 \times 3$ (b) $3^2 \times 7^2$
   (c) $2^4 \times 3 \times 11^2$ (d) $2^3 \times 5 \times 7^2 \times 11$
5. (a) 43   (b) 71   (c) $35\frac{9}{11}$ (d) $338\frac{2}{27}$.

EXERCISE 2   *page 26*

1. (a) 21   (b) 8   (c) 22   (d) 36
2. (a) 24   (b) 24   (c) 108   (d) 4840
   (e) 60   (f) 252   (g) 560
3. 1320   4. £6
5. 25 ft. = 300 in.; 3 ft. 9 in. = 45 in.; H.C.F. = 15. ∴Tiles
   are 15 in. square. Number of tiles is 60.
6. 72 secs.   7. L.C.M. of 1, 2, 3 ... 10 = 2520.   8. 16.

CHAPTER 4

EXERCISE I   *page 30*

1. 16 hr.   2. 48 min.   3. 3 pt.
4. 84 sec. (= 1 min. 24 sec.)   5. 6 min. 24 sec.   6. 8s. 9d.
7. $\frac{5}{24}$ 8. $\frac{1}{6}$ 9. $\frac{5}{8}$
10. $\frac{7}{13}$ 11. $\frac{25}{36}$.

EXERCISE 2   *page 32*

1. $1\frac{1}{4}$ 2. $\frac{1}{8}$ 3. $4\frac{1}{10}$
4. $1\frac{1}{8}$ 5. $1\frac{3}{4}$ 6. $6\frac{1}{11}$
7. $1\frac{17}{20}$ 8. $2\frac{11}{44}$ 9. $\frac{29}{60}$
10. $\frac{24}{25}$ 11. $1\frac{31}{34}$ 12. $1\frac{1}{6}$.

EXERCISE 3   *page 35*

1. $\frac{8}{11}$ 2. $\frac{5}{8}$ 3. $3\frac{3}{8}$

4. $\frac{9}{16}$ 5. $35\frac{3}{4}$ 6. **2**

7. $\frac{1}{6}$ 8. $1\frac{1}{3}$ 9. $2\frac{2}{3}$

10. $1\frac{1}{2}$ 11. $\frac{1}{2}$ 12. $1\frac{23}{147}$

13. $\frac{9}{25}$ 14. 2.

EXERCISE 4   *page* 37

1. $1\frac{4}{15}$ 2. 17   3. $\frac{42}{505}$

4. $\frac{2}{65}$ 5. $1\frac{11}{32}$ 6. $\frac{7}{17}$.

EXERCISE 5   *page* 38

1. $\frac{11}{29}$ 2. £4500   3. £375   4. $2\frac{3}{10}$

5. 17 days   6. 24 mi.   7. $56\frac{1}{4}$ min.   8. 12s. 8d.

CHAPTER 5

EXERCISE 1   *page* 41

1. 14s. $8\frac{1}{2}$d.   2. 15s. 7d.   3. £2 14s. 8d.

4. £68 2s. 9d.   5. £481 18s. 3d.   6. £3502 4s. 8d.

7. 3s. $11\frac{1}{4}$d.   8. 5s. $8\frac{3}{4}$d.   9. 2s. $5\frac{3}{4}$d.

10. £1 12s. 11d.   11. £7 12s. $10\frac{1}{2}$d.   12. £96 5s. $9\frac{1}{2}$d.

13. £2 16s. 10d.   14. £18 18s. 9d.

EXERCISE 2   *page* 43

1. 1856d.   2. 4030d.   3. 49,073d.

4. 694f.   5. 2381f.   6. 84,355f.

7. £16 15s. 3d.   8. £91 13s. 2d.   9. £75 8s. $1\frac{1}{2}$d.

10. £49 3s. $7\frac{1}{2}$d.   11. £6 4s. $6\frac{1}{4}$d.   12. £897 6s. $4\frac{1}{4}$d.

13. 41   14. 1594 articles: 1s. $3\frac{1}{2}$d. change   15. 144.

EXERCISE 3   *page* 47

1. £113 9s. 9d.   2. £212 5s. 0d.   3. £2247 9s. $10\frac{3}{4}$d.

4. £12,550 13s. 6d.   5. £182 18s. 8d.   6. £148 10s.

7. £9322 16s.   8. £11,366 9s. $4\frac{1}{2}$d.   9. £109 18s. 8d.

10. £270 18s. 5d.   11. £2099 3s. $6\frac{1}{2}$d.   12. £24,063 11s. 5d.

13. £1346 12s. 8d.   14. £99 12s. $10\frac{1}{2}$d.   15. £798

16. £8885 17s. 11d.   17. £240 14s. $3\frac{1}{2}$d.   18. £337 1s. $2\frac{1}{2}$d.

19. £17 14s. 2d.   20. £1 10s. 7d.

EXERCISE 4   *page* 48

1. £5 6s. 5d.   2. £3 10s. 6d.

3. £6 18s. 7d., rem. 4d.   4. £87 3s. $2\frac{1}{2}$d.

5. 15s. 11d.   6. $9\frac{3}{4}$d.

7. £12 7s. 8d.   8. £4 1s. 8d. (nearest 1d.)

9. £20 11s. 9d., rem. 3d.   10. £9 16s. 1d.
11. £17 2s. 11d.   12. £19 4s. 2d., rem. 3s. 4d.
13. £457 14s. 6d.   14. £2 6s. 6d.
15. £15 12s. 4d.   16. £545 4s. 0¼d.
17. ⅛   18. $\frac{77}{100}$.

CHAPTER 6

EXERCISE 1   *page* 51
1. (a) 541 lb.   (b) 3047 lb.   (c) 13,216 lb.   (d) 10,910 lb.
2. (a) 3530 ft.   (b) 13,860 ft. (c) 702 ft.   (d) 2697 ft.
3. (a) 120 pt.   (b) 1248 pt.
4. 604,800 sec.   5. 63360 in.   6. 24120 in.
7. (a) 1 yd. 0 ft. 11 in.   (b) 5 yd. 2 ft. 5 in.   (c) 20 yd. 0 ft. 8 in.
8. (a) 1 mi. 2 fur. 1 ch. 8 in.   (b) 3 mi. 2 fur. 4 ch. 8 yd.
   (c) 2 mi. 3 fur. 2 ch. 11 yd.
9. (a) 4 cwt. 2 qr. 15 lb.   (b) 1 ton 18 cwt. 0 qr. 25¼ lb.
   (c) 35 ton 0 cwt. 3 qr. 16 lb.
10. (a) 16 hr. 40 min.   (b) 23 hr. 46 min. 30 sec.
    (c) 11 days 13 hr. 46 min. 40 sec.
11. (a) 1 qr. 7 bush. 2 pk. 1 gall.
    (b) 4 qr. 6 bush. 2 pk. 1 gall. 0 qt. 1 pt.
    (c) 2 qr. 7 bush. 0 pk. 1 gall. 3 qt. 1 pt.
12. (a) $\frac{13}{133}$ (b) ⅕ (c) ⅙ (d) ½ (e) $\frac{772}{11521}$ (f) $\frac{35}{408}$
13. 9 curtains; 4 ft. 6 in. left over.

EXERCISE 2   *page* 54
1. (a) 6 days 7 hr. 24 min.   (b) 4 mi. 0 fur. 2 ch. 7 yd.
   (c) 1 qr. 1 bush.
2. (a) 12 hr. 57 min. 58 sec.   (b) 6 yd. 1 ft. 10 in.
   (c) 5 fur. 0 ch. 16 yd.   (d) 2 ton 6 cwt. 0 qr. 10 lb.
3. (a) 4 fur. 2 ch. 17 yd. 1 ft.   (b) 12 days 2 hr. 28 min. 24 sec.
   (c) 3 cwt. 2 qr. 7 lb. 7 oz.   (d) 10 oz. 12 dwt. 8 gr.
4. (a) 12 cwt. 2 qr. 20 lb.
   (b) 6 hr. 33 min. 55 sec. (to nearest second)
   (c) 53 yd. 1 ft. 2 in. (to nearest inch)
5. 7481 hr. (nearest hour)   6. 2325 min.
7. 8 ton 2 cwt.; 17 cwt. 1 qr.   8. 2 ton 0 cwt. 1 qr.

EXERCISE 3   *page* 56
1. £2 10s. 7½d.   2. £1 19s. 2¼d.   3. £10 15s. 8¾d.

4. £56 10s. 3d.   5. £139 7s. 8d. (to nearest 1d.)
6. £163 4s. 2d. (to nearest 1d.)   7. £50 4s. 6d.

CHAPTER 7

EXERCISE 1   *page* 59

1. (a) 2·3   (b) 6·01   (c) 37·57   (d) 0·91
   (e) 0·07   (f) 0·0004   (g) 85·076
2. (a) $6 + \frac{8}{10}$ (b) $10 + 4 + \frac{9}{10} + \frac{2}{100}$ (c) $200 + 7 + \frac{4}{100}$
   (d) $\frac{6}{10}$ (e) $\frac{9}{100} + \frac{4}{1000}$ (f) $1000 + \frac{1}{1000}$
3. (a) 31·262   (b) 330·614   (c) 2013·5   (d) 1470·8004
4. (a) 23·7   (b) 13·75   (c) 9·073   (d) 297·9155.

EXERCISE 2   *page* 65

1. 417   2. 0·087   3. 22·010   4. 6·1
5. 0·0070   6. 0·0309   7. 9·84   8. 0·098.

EXERCISE 3   *page* 65

1. (a) 0·4   (b) 63   (c) 3850   (d) 7
   (e) 0·15   (f) 7·08   (g) 1·6   (h) 492
   (i) 5·04   (j) 2023   (k) 222·64   (l) 0·0053
2. (a) 3·4   (b) 1·45   (c) 0·325   (d) 0·0008
   (e) 0·192   (f) 1·14   (g) 0·193   (h) 5·5
   (i) 5400   (j) 180   (k) 0·003652 (l) 28·3
3. (a) 93·86   (b) 0·2856   (c) 27·8064   (d) 11·22
   (e) 2500   (f) 507   (g) 3599·8   (h) 17·60   (i) 14·23
4. (a) 0·89   (b) 0·073   (c) 1·39   (d) 22·0
   (e) 0·0084   (f) 22·470.

EXERCISE 4   *page* 68

1. (a) 0·6   (b) 0·625   (c) 0·6364   (d) 0·2222
   (e) 0·3889   (f) 0·5294
2. (a) $\frac{3}{25}$ (b) $\frac{179}{250}$ (c) $\frac{17}{200}$ (d) $\frac{453}{5000}$ (e) $7\frac{13}{80}$
3. $\frac{427}{125} = 3·416$, $\frac{147}{43} = 3·419$, $\frac{171}{50} = 3·420$
4. (a) £7·6333   (b) £16·2604   (c) £203·8927
5. (a) £2·971   (b) £0·94375   (c) £61·90833
6. (a) £21 14s. 10d.   (b) 13s. 9d.   (c) 4s. 4d.   (d) £7 14s. 2d.
7. 19s. 11d. (to nearest 1d.).

EXERCISE 5   *page* 72

1. 9·35 m.   2. 101 mi. 1601 yd.   3. (a) $\frac{1}{25}$ (b) 54
4. 10·0 lb.   5. 45 m.   6. 52·8 m.p.h.   7. 1990 c.c.
8. (a) 51·2 ares   (b) 0·512 Ha.   10. 4s. 6d.

CHAPTER 8

EXERCISE 1 *page* 74

1. 3:32　　2. 3:2　　3. 5:6　　4. 15:16　　5. 5:3
6. £4 16s.　　7. 23:17　　8. 3:2　　9. 0·20625　　10. 60
11. £1608, £1206, £804　　12. 7:6

EXERCISE 2 *page* 79

1. £34 4s.　　　　2. 16 min.　　　3. £1920
4. 37⅗ days　　　5. £73 1s. 3d.　　6. 46 men.

EXERCISE 3 *page* 80

1. £20; £16 13s. 4d.; £10; £3 6s. 8d.
2. £100 each man, £75 each woman.
3. £7 10s.; £11 5s.; £13 10s.　　4. The first.
5. 17½ min.　　　　　6. 17:9; £41 11s. 7d.

EXERCISE 4 *page* 83

1. £632　　2. 9s. 11d. (to nearest 1d.)　　3. 1:3·864
4. 30 min.　　5. 7 st. 4½ lb.　6. 42·1 m.p.h.　7. 30 runs.

CHAPTER 9

EXERCISE 1 *page* 86

1. (a) 20%　　　　(b) 25%　　　　(c) 66⅔%
　(d) 63$\frac{7}{11}$%　　　(e) 112·5%　　　(f) 0·429%
2. (a) $\frac{3}{20}$　　　　(b) $\frac{7}{25}$　　　　(c) $\frac{11}{40}$
　(d) 1$\frac{3}{5}$　　　　(e) $\frac{1}{3}$　　　　(f) $\frac{1}{250}$
3. (a) 0·35　　　　(b) 0·3333　　　(c) 1·075
　(d) 0·0375　　　(e) 0·0164　　　(f) 0·0343
4. (a) 31$\frac{1}{9}$%　(b) 12½%　(c) 14%　(d) 66⅔%　(e) 12½%
5. (a) £9　(b) £1 18s. 3d.　(c) 4 16 pt.　(d) 6s. 0·72d.
　(e) £2 12s. 4d.

EXERCISE 2 *page* 90

1. (a) £4 16s.　　(b) £4 6s. 3d.　　(c) 10s.
2. (a) 12½% profit　(b) 25% loss　　(c) 33⅓% profit.
3. (a) £2 10s.　　(b) £4　　　　(c) £1 0s. 6d.
4. (a) 3s. 11d.　　(b) 3s. 11d.　　(c) 8s. 3d.
5. 0·92%　　　6. £54　　　　7. 3·575%
8. 0·1125%; £4 15s. 7½d.

EXERCISE 3 *page* 94

1. £491 6s.　　2. 7¾%　　3. 8%　　4. £1 11s. 4d.

5. 9·375%   6. (a) 19·8%   (b) 14s. 8d.   7. 10·53%
8. £561 12s.; 8%.

EXERCISE 4
                                                        page 96
  1. 7:13   2. 8s. 3d. (to nearest 1d.)   3. 42⁴⁄₇%
  4. 35%   5. 2:1   6. 31   7. 38.

CHAPTER 10
EXERCISE 1   *page* 102
  1. 104° F.; 15·6° C.   2. 51·8 ft.; 2·17 sec.
  3. 11·23 a.m.; 141 mi.
  4. £8400; advertising costs eventually outweigh resultant profits.

EXERCISE 2   *page* 106
  1. Median is 1·3 children per family
  3. Median height 5 ft. 7·4 in.; mean height 5 ft. 8·9 in.

CHAPTER 11
EXERCISE 1   *page* 110
  1. 70 sq. in.   2. 2½ sq. ft.   3. 408 sq. cm.   4. 15¾ sq. ft.
  5. 9 sq. ft. 68 sq. in.   6. 756 sq. yd.   7. 28 sq. yd. 4 sq. ft.
  8. 34 in.; 7 ft.; 82 cm.; 21 ft. 6 in.; 12 ft. 6 in.; 136 yd.
  9. 22 ft.   10. 16 ft.   11. 220 yd.; 550 yd.   12. 90 sq. in.

EXERCISE 2   *page* 113
  1. (a) 36 sq. in.   (b) 36½ sq. in.   (c) 85½ sq. in.
  2. 30 sq. in.   3. 798 sq. ft.; 266 turves; £4 8s. 8d.
  4. 423¾ sq. ft.; 7 pieces; no, with care 4 pieces for side walls and
     3 pieces for end walls would do, but observe that, for rooms
     of different shape, this might not be true.
  5. 12⅝ sq. ft.   6. 45 sq. ft. 118 sq. in.; 17s. 2d. (to nearest 1d.).

EXERCISE 3   *page* 117
  1. 37 cu. yd.; 27·9 ton.   2. 12 min.   3. 4 mm.
  4. 25·32 ton   5. 1498 cu. in.   6. £3 10s.

EXERCISE 4   *page* 122
  1. (a) 27 sq. in. (b) 4·5 sq. cm.   2. 16 in.
  3. 8 sq. ft. 23 sq. in.   4. 20⅝ cu. ft.; 128·9 gall.
  5. 5467 bricks   6. 800 lb.

EXERCISE 5 *page* 126

1. 73   2. 962   3. 3016   4. 1·414
5. 4·102   6. 2·222   7. 14·83   8. 80·14
9. 0·6301   10. 0·2417   11. 0·08695   12. 0·02780.

EXERCISE 6 *page* 129

1. (*a*) 29   (*b*) 12   (*c*) 60   (*d*) 53
2. 65   3. 7·616   4. 19·26   5. 519·9
6. 104·6   7. 1·122   8. 16·52   9. 21 ft. 5 in.
10. 6 ft. 6 in.; 47 sq. ft. 18 sq. in.
11. £8 17s. 7d.   12. 3 ch. 3 yd. 2 ft.   13. 6·403 in.

CHAPTER 12

EXERCISE 1 *page* 138

1. (*a*) 0·7782   (*b*) 0·9638   (*c*) 1·4914   (*d*) 0·2148
   (*e*) 0·8603   (*f*) 0·8116   (*g*) 1·9355   (*h*) 1·2945
   (*i*) 0·6852   (*j*) 1·5106   (*k*) 2·5014   (*l*) 0·0203
   (*m*) 5·2148   (*n*) 0·9955   (*o*) 3·7364   (*p*) 1·8511
2. log 6·5 = 0·81, log 3·7 = 0·57, log 8·3 = 0·92 } correct to 2
   0·42 = log 2·6, 0·59 = log 3·9, 0·20 = log 1·6 } sig. fig.

EXERCISE 2 *page* 140

1. (*a*) 4·125   (*b*) 2·017   (*c*) 7·934   (*d*) 1·004
   (*e*) 18·62   (*f*) 12·05   (*g*) 293·6   (*h*) 40,000
   (*i*) 9·725   (*j*) 6·009   (*k*) 2622   (*l*) 324,300.

EXERCISE 3 *page* 141

1. 31·85   2. 125·9   3. 888·8   4. 34·53
5. 7·006   6. 91,180   7. 3·930   8. 1·052
9. 5·194   10. 183·1   11. 3·753   12. 1539
13. 15·46   14. 1·789   15. 14·66   16. 4·990
17. 1·539   18. 10570   19. 1304   20. 8·474.

EXERCISE 4 *page* 143

1. (*a*) 0 (*b*) $\bar{1}$ (*c*) 4 (*d*) 4 (*e*) $\bar{2}$ (*f*) $\bar{5}$ (*g*) $\bar{2}$
2. (*a*) $\bar{1}$·3412   (*b*) $\bar{2}$·7993   (*c*) $\bar{4}$·3381   (*d*) $\bar{4}$·9789
   (*e*) $\bar{2}$·9586   (*f*) $\bar{1}$·9364   (*g*) $\bar{7}$·7924
3. (*a*) 441·6   (*b*) 0·04416   (*c*) 0·9632   (*d*) 0·0005333
   (*e*) 7,943,000   (*f*) 0·008489   (*g*) 0·1023   (*h*) 0·000000587.

EXERCISE 5
page 145

1. 1·769   2. 0·3685   3. 1·551   4. 0·001174
5. 0·8798   6. 0·3122   7. 0·08958   8. 0·009811
9. 0·3533   10. 0·004270   11. 2·179   12. 190·4
13. 80·04   14. 0·1607   15. 0·5347   16. 0·7711.

EXERCISE 6
page 148

1. —0·105   2. 1·66   3. 3·021   4. (i) 20·1, (ii) 793, (iii) 170
5. 28·8   6. (i) 137·(5), (ii) 6·61   7. 9·33   8. 2·51.

CHAPTER 13

EXERCISE 1
page 152

1. (a) 8·8 in.   (b) 66 in.   (c) $25\frac{1}{7}$ in.   (d) 22 ft.
2. (a) 55·4 sq. cm.   (b) 616 sq. in.
   (c) 28·3 sq. in.   (d) 78·6 sq. cm.
3. 7·90 in.; 24·8 in.   4. 6·58 in.   5. 5 ft. (to nearest inch)
6. 11.   7. 776   8. 165 (3 sig. fig.).

EXERCISE 2
page 158

1. 26·1 cu. yd.   2. 1·70 in.   3. 1·96 cu. ft.   4. 353 lb.
5. 161 sq. in.   6. 9·42 cu. ft.; 22·0 sq. ft.
7. Take 17 pennies; 0·0798 cu. in.   8. 7 min. 12 sec.

EXERCISE 3
page 162

1. (a) $183\frac{1}{3}$ cu. in.   (b) $314\frac{2}{7}$ cu. in.   (c) 5·13 cu. in.
2. (a) 32·7 sq. in.   (b) 33·2(5) sq. in.   (c) 28·1 sq. cm.
3. 126·7 sq. cm.   4. 530 cu. ft.   5. 3972 tons   6. 0·59 in.

EXERCISE 4
page 164

1. (a) 180 c.c.; 154 sq. cm.   (b) 113 cu. in.; 113 sq. in.
   (c) 4·19 cu. in.; 12·6 sq. in.   (d) 2500 cu. in.; 891 sq. in.
2. 0·985 cm.   3. 0·892 in.   4. 25·3 sq. in.
5. 0·496 in.   6. 771 cu. ft.

CHAPTER 14

EXERCISE 1
page 169

1. £72   2. £28 10s.   3. £90 13s.
4. £512   5. £17 16s. 2d.   6. £5 19s. 5d.
7. £58 11s. 9d.   8. £500   9. $8\frac{1}{8}$%
10. £233 6s. 8d.   11. 8 years   12. £96 10s. 1d.
13. £2 1s.   14. £1040.

EXERCISE 2 *page* 172
1. £65 12s.   2. £218 10s. 3d.   3. £15 3s. 4d.
4. £138 0s. 8d.   5. £90 15s. 5d.   6. £44 3s. 8d.
7. (a) 7s. 2d.   (b) £25 8s. 3d.

EXERCISE 3 *page* 176
1. £652 15s. 11d.   2. £1954 13s. 6d.   3. £1122 9s. 1d.
4. £606 12s. 7d.   5. £1068   6. £2821
7. £157   8. £7420   9. 4·6%
10. 17·7 years   11. 5%.

CHAPTER 15

EXERCISE 1 *page* 180
1. £48 1s. 4d.   2. 12s. 2·25d.
3. 16s. 3·52d.   4. £7766 13s. 4d.

EXERCISE 2 *page* 189
1. £129 2s. 6d.   2. £143 11s. 6d.
3. £159 6s.; £40, £17   4. £33 3s.; £27 10s. 4d.

CHAPTER 16

EXERCISE 1 *page* 197
1. £1250 stock; £37 10s.   2. 4⅙%; £16 13s. 4d.
3. 3½% War Stock   4. £90 12s. 6d.; £10
5. £6 18s. 3d.%   6. 23s. 4d.
7. 12½%   8. £544; £1 16s. 3d. less
9. 988 shares   10. 1040 shares; £39.

EXERCISE 2 *page* 204
1. £384 18s.   2. £1634 8s.   3. £2162 8s.
4. £320 6s.   5. 61 shares; £13 14s. 6d.; 4·9%.

EXERCISE 3 *page* 206
1. £60 10s.   2. £12 18s. 9d.   3. £33 18s. 11d.

CHAPTER 17

EXERCISE 1 *page* 213
1. (a) 1110   (b) 100010   (c) 11001101
    (d) 1000100110l   (e) 100101001011O
2. (a) 6   (b) 3   (c) 21   (d) 38   (e) 459

3. (a) 100001; 33
   (c) 110111101; 445

   (b) 1000111; 71
   (d) 1000001000010; 4162

4. 1100110   5. 119

6. 11110

7. (a) 11001111; 207
   (c) 111000111000; 3640
   (e) 1011100011001010; 47306

   (b) 1110010100; 1836
   (d) 10001100011100; 8988

8. 1111000 r. 1101; $120\frac{13}{18}$

9. 1011 r. 1100; $11\frac{12}{19}$.

LOGARITHMS of numbers 1000 to 5499

	0	1	2	3	4	5	6	7	8	9	1	2	3	4	5	6	7	8	9
10	0000	0043	0086	0128	0170	0212	0253	0294	0334	0374	4	8	12	17	21	25	29	33	37
11	0414	0453	0492	0531	0569	0607	0645	0682	0719	0755	4	8	11	15	19	23	26	30	34
12	0792	0828	0864	0899	0934	0969	1004	1038	1072	1106	3	7	10	14	17	21	24	28	31
13	1139	1173	1206	1239	1271	1303	1335	1367	1399	1430	3	6	10	13	16	19	23	26	29
14	1461	1492	1523	1553	1584	1614	1644	1673	1703	1732	3	6	9	12	15	18	21	24	27
15	1761	1790	1818	1847	1875	1903	1931	1959	1987	2014	3	6	8	11	14	17	20	22	25
16	2041	2068	2095	2122	2148	2175	2201	2227	2253	2279	3	5	8	11	13	16	18	21	24
17	2304	2330	2355	2380	2405	2430	2455	2480	2504	2529	2	5	7	10	12	15	17	20	22
18	2553	2577	2601	2625	2648	2672	2695	2718	2742	2765	2	5	7	9	12	14	16	19	21
19	2788	2810	2833	2856	2878	2900	2923	2945	2967	2989	2	4	7	9	11	13	16	18	20
20	3010	3032	3054	3075	3096	3118	3139	3160	3181	3201	2	4	6	8	11	13	15	17	19
21	3222	3243	3263	3284	3304	3324	3345	3365	3385	3404	2	4	6	8	10	12	14	16	18
22	3424	3444	3464	3483	3502	3522	3541	3560	3579	3598	2	4	6	8	10	12	14	15	17
23	3617	3636	3655	3674	3692	3711	3729	3747	3766	3784	2	4	6	7	9	11	13	15	17
24	3802	3820	3838	3856	3874	3892	3909	3927	3945	3962	2	4	5	7	9	11	12	14	16
25	3979	3997	4014	4031	4048	4065	4082	4099	4116	4133	2	3	5	7	9	10	12	14	15
26	4150	4166	4183	4200	4216	4232	4249	4265	4281	4298	2	3	5	7	8	10	11	13	15
27	4314	4330	4346	4362	4378	4393	4409	4425	4440	4456	2	3	5	6	8	9	11	13	14
28	4472	4487	4502	4518	4533	4548	4564	4579	4594	4609	2	3	5	6	8	9	11	12	14
29	4624	4639	4654	4669	4683	4698	4713	4728	4742	4757	1	3	4	6	7	9	10	12	13
30	4771	4786	4800	4814	4829	4843	4857	4871	4886	4900	1	3	4	6	7	9	10	11	13
31	4914	4928	4942	4955	4969	4983	4997	5011	5024	5038	1	3	4	5	7	8	10	11	12
32	5051	5065	5079	5092	5105	5119	5132	5145	5159	5172	1	3	4	5	7	8	9	11	12
33	5185	5198	5211	5224	5237	5250	5263	5276	5289	5302	1	3	4	5	6	8	9	10	12
34	5315	5328	5340	5353	5366	5378	5391	5403	5416	5428	1	3	4	5	6	8	9	10	11
35	5441	5453	5465	5478	5490	5502	5514	5527	5539	5551	1	2	4	5	6	7	9	10	11
36	5563	5575	5587	5599	5611	5623	5635	5647	5658	5670	1	2	4	5	6	7	8	10	11
37	5632	5694	5705	5717	5729	5740	5752	5763	5775	5786	1	2	3	5	6	7	8	9	10
38	5798	5809	5821	5832	5843	5855	5866	5877	5888	5899	1	2	3	5	6	7	8	9	10
39	5911	5922	5933	5944	5955	5966	5977	5988	5999	6010	1	2	3	4	5	7	8	9	10
40	6021	6031	6042	6053	6064	6075	6085	6096	6107	6117	1	2	3	4	5	6	7	9	10
41	6128	6138	6149	6160	6170	6180	6191	6201	6212	6222	1	2	3	4	5	6	7	8	9
42	6232	6243	6253	6263	6274	6284	6294	6304	6314	6325	1	2	3	4	5	6	7	8	9
43	6335	6345	6355	6365	6375	6385	6395	6405	6415	6425	1	2	3	4	5	6	7	8	9
44	6435	6444	6454	6464	6474	6484	6493	6503	6513	6522	1	2	3	4	5	6	7	8	9
45	6532	6542	6551	6561	6571	6580	6590	6599	6609	6618	1	2	3	4	5	6	7	8	9
46	6628	6637	6646	6656	6665	6675	6684	6693	6702	6712	1	2	3	4	5	6	7	7	8
47	6721	6730	6739	6749	6758	6767	6776	6785	6794	6803	1	2	3	4	5	5	6	7	8
48	6812	6821	6830	6839	6848	6857	6866	6875	6884	6893	1	2	3	4	4	5	6	7	8
49	6902	6911	6920	6928	6937	6946	6955	6964	6972	6981	1	2	3	4	4	5	6	7	8
50	6990	6998	7007	7016	7024	7033	7042	7050	7059	7067	1	2	3	3	4	5	6	7	8
51	7076	7084	7093	7101	7110	7118	7126	7135	7143	7152	1	2	3	3	4	5	6	7	8
52	7160	7168	7177	7185	7193	7202	7210	7218	7226	7235	1	2	2	3	4	5	6	7	7
53	7243	7251	7259	7267	7275	7284	7292	7300	7308	7316	1	2	2	3	4	5	6	6	7
54	7324	7332	7340	7348	7356	7364	7372	7380	7388	7396	1	2	2	3	4	5	6	6	7
	0	1	2	3	4	5	6	7	8	9	1	2	3	4	5	6	7	8	9

LOGARITHMS of numbers 5500 to 9999

Proportional Parts

	0	1	2	3	4	5	6	7	8	9	1	2	3	4	5	6	7	8	9
55	7404	7412	7419	7427	7435	7443	7451	7459	7466	7474	1	2	2	3	4	5	5	6	7
56	7482	7490	7497	7505	7513	7520	7528	7536	7543	7551	1	2	2	3	4	5	5	6	7
57	7559	7566	7574	7582	7589	7597	7604	7612	7619	7627	1	2	2	3	4	5	5	6	7
58	7634	7642	7649	7657	7664	7672	7679	7686	7694	7701	1	1	2	3	4	4	5	6	7
59	7709	7716	7723	7731	7738	7745	7752	7760	7767	7774	1	1	2	3	4	4	5	6	7
60	7782	7789	7796	7803	7810	7818	7825	7832	7839	7846	1	1	2	3	4	4	5	6	6
61	7853	7860	7868	7875	7882	7889	7896	7903	7910	7917	1	1	2	3	4	4	5	6	6
62	7924	7931	7938	7945	7952	7959	7966	7973	7980	7987	1	1	2	3	3	4	5	6	6
63	7993	8000	8007	8014	8021	8028	8035	8041	8048	8055	1	1	2	3	3	4	5	6	6
64	8062	8069	8075	8082	8089	8096	8102	8109	8116	8122	1	1	2	3	3	4	5	5	6
65	8129	8136	8142	8149	8156	8162	8169	8176	8182	8189	1	1	2	3	3	4	5	5	6
66	8195	8202	8209	8215	8222	8228	8235	8241	8248	8254	1	1	2	3	3	4	5	5	6
67	8261	8267	8274	8280	8287	8293	8299	8306	8312	8319	1	1	2	3	3	4	4	5	6
68	8325	8331	8338	8344	8351	8357	8363	8370	8376	8382	1	1	2	3	3	4	4	5	6
69	8388	8395	8401	8407	8414	8420	8426	8432	8439	8445	1	1	2	3	3	4	4	5	6
70	8451	8457	8463	8470	8476	8482	8488	8494	8500	8506	1	1	2	2	3	4	4	5	6
71	8513	8519	8525	8531	8537	8543	8549	8555	8561	8567	1	1	2	2	3	4	4	5	5
72	8573	8579	8585	8591	8597	8603	8609	8615	8621	8627	1	1	2	2	3	4	4	5	5
73	8633	8639	8645	8651	8657	8663	8669	8675	8681	8686	1	1	2	2	3	4	4	5	5
74	8692	8698	8704	8710	8716	8722	8727	8733	8739	8745	1	1	2	2	3	4	4	5	5
75	8751	8756	8762	8768	8774	8779	8785	8791	8797	8802	1	1	2	2	3	3	4	5	.5
76	8808	8814	8820	8825	8831	8837	8842	8848	8854	8859	1	1	2	2	3	3	4	5	5
77	8865	8871	8876	8882	8887	8893	8899	8904	8910	8915	1	1	2	2	3	3	4	4	5
78	8921	8927	8932	8938	8943	8949	8954	8960	8965	8971	1	1	2	2	3	3	4	4	5
79	8976	8982	8987	8993	8998	9004	9009	9015	9020	9025	1	1	2	2	3	3	4	4	5
80	9031	9036	9042	9047	9053	9058	9063	9069	9074	9079	1	1	2	2	3	3	4	4	5
81	9085	9090	9096	9101	9106	9112	9117	9122	9128	9133	1	1	2	2	3	3	4	4	5
82	9138	9143	9149	9154	9159	9165	9170	9175	9180	9186	1	1	2	2	3	3	4	4	5
83	9191	9196	9201	9206	9212	9217	9222	9227	9232	9238	1	1	2	2	3	3	4	4	5
84	9243	9248	9253	9258	9263	9269	9274	9279	9284	9289	1	1	2	2	3	3	4	4	5
85	9294	9299	9304	9309	9315	9320	9325	9330	9335	9340	1	1	2	2	3	3	4	4	5
86	9345	9350	9355	9360	9365	9370	9375	9380	9385	9390	1	1	2	2	3	3	4	4	5
87	9395	9400	9405	9410	9415	9420	9425	9430	9435	9440	0	1	1	2	2	3	3	4	4
88	9445	9450	9455	9460	9465	9469	9474	9479	9484	9489	0	1	1	2	2	3	3	4	4
89	9494	9499	9504	9509	9513	9518	9523	9528	9533	9538	0	1	1	2	2	3	3	4	4
90	9542	9547	9552	9557	9562	9566	9571	9576	9581	9586	0	1	1	2	2	3	3	4	4
91	9590	9595	9600	9605	9609	9614	9619	9624	9628	9633	0	1	1	2	2	3	3	4	4
92	9638	9643	9647	9652	9657	9661	9666	9671	9675	9680	0	1	1	2	2	3	3	4	4
93	9685	9689	9694	9699	9703	9708	9713	9717	9722	9727	0	1	1	2	2	3	3	4	4
94	9731	9736	9741	9745	9750	9754	9759	9764	9768	9773	0	1	1	2	2	3	3	4	4
95	9777	9782	9786	9791	9795	9800	9805	9809	9814	9818	0	1	1	2	2	3	3	4	4
96	9823	9827	9832	9836	9841	9845	9850	9854	9859	9863	0	1	1	2	2	3	3	4	4
97	9868	9872	9877	9881	9886	9890	9894	9899	9903	9908	0	1	1	2	2	3	3	4	4
98	9912	9917	9921	9926	9930	9934	9939	9943	9948	9952	0	1	1	2	2	3	3	4	4
99	9956	9961	9965	9969	9974	9978	9983	9987	9991	9996	0	1	1	2	2	3	3	4	4
	0	1	2	3	4	5	6	7	8	9	1	2	3	4	5	6	7	8	9

ANTI-LOGARITHMS

	0	1	2	3	4	5	6	7	8	9	1	2	3	4	5	6	7	8	9
·00	1000	1002	1005	1007	1009	1012	1014	1016	1019	1021	0	0	1	1	1	1	2	2	2
·01	1023	1026	1028	1030	1033	1035	1038	1040	1042	1045	0	0	1	1	1	1	2	2	2
·02	1047	1050	1052	1054	1057	1059	1062	1064	1067	1069	0	0	1	1	1	1	2	2	2
·03	1072	1074	1076	1079	1081	1084	1086	1089	1091	1094	0	0	1	1	1	1	2	2	2
·04	1096	1099	1102	1104	1107	1109	1112	1114	1117	1119	0	1	1	1	1	2	2	2	2
·05	1122	1125	1127	1130	1132	1135	1138	1140	1143	1146	0	1	1	1	1	2	2	2	2
·06	1148	1151	1153	1156	1159	1161	1164	1167	1169	1172	0	1	1	1	1	2	2	2	2
·07	1175	1178	1180	1183	1186	1189	1191	1194	1197	1199	0	1	1	1	1	2	2	2	2
·08	1202	1205	1208	1211	1213	1216	1219	1222	1225	1227	0	1	1	1	1	2	2	2	3
·09	1230	1233	1236	1239	1242	1245	1247	1250	1253	1256	0	1	1	1	1	2	2	2	3
·10	1259	1262	1265	1268	1271	1274	1276	1279	1282	1285	0	1	1	1	1	2	2	2	3
·11	1288	1291	1294	1297	1300	1303	1306	1309	1312	1315	0	1	1	1	2	2	2	2	3
·12	1318	1321	1324	1327	1330	1334	1337	1340	1343	1346	0	1	1	1	2	2	2	2	3
·13	1349	1352	1355	1358	1361	1365	1368	1371	1374	1377	0	1	1	1	2	2	2	2	3
·14	1380	1384	1387	1390	1393	1396	1400	1403	1406	1409	0	1	1	1	2	2	2	3	3
·15	1413	1416	1419	1422	1426	1429	1432	1435	1439	1442	0	1	1	1	2	2	2	3	3
·16	1445	1449	1452	1455	1459	1462	1466	1469	1472	1476	0	1	1	1	2	2	2	3	3
·17	1479	1483	1486	1489	1493	1496	1500	1503	1507	1510	0	1	1	1	2	2	2	3	3
·18	1514	1517	1521	1524	1528	1531	1535	1538	1542	1545	0	1	1	1	2	2	2	3	3
·19	1549	1552	1556	1560	1563	1567	1570	1574	1578	1581	0	1	1	1	2	2	3	3	3
·20	1585	1589	1592	1596	1600	1603	1607	1611	1614	1618	0	1	1	1	2	2	3	3	3
·21	1622	1626	1629	1633	1637	1641	1644	1648	1652	1656	0	1	1	2	2	2	3	3	3
·22	1660	1663	1667	1671	1675	1679	1683	1687	1690	1694	0	1	1	2	2	2	3	3	3
·23	1698	1702	1706	1710	1714	1718	1722	1726	1730	1734	0	1	1	2	2	2	3	3	4
·24	1738	1742	1746	1750	1754	1758	1762	1766	1770	1774	0	1	1	2	2	2	3	3	4
·25	1778	1782	1786	1791	1795	1799	1803	1807	1811	1816	0	1	1	2	2	3	3	3	4
·26	1820	1824	1828	1832	1837	1841	1845	1849	1854	1858	0	1	1	2	2	3	3	3	4
·27	1862	1866	1871	1875	1879	1884	1888	1892	1897	1901	0	1	1	2	2	3	3	3	4
·28	1905	1910	1914	1919	1923	1928	1932	1936	1941	1945	0	1	1	2	2	3	3	4	4
·29	1950	1954	1959	1963	1968	1972	1977	1982	1986	1991	0	1	1	2	2	3	3	4	4
·30	1995	2000	2004	2009	2014	2018	2023	2028	2032	2037	0	1	1	2	2	3	3	4	4
·31	2042	2046	2051	2056	2061	2065	2070	2075	2080	2084	0	1	1	2	2	3	3	4	4
·32	2089	2094	2099	2104	2109	2113	2118	2123	2128	2133	0	1	1	2	2	3	3	4	4
·33	2138	2143	2148	2153	2158	2163	2173	2178	2183		0	1	1	2	2	3	3	4	4
·34	2188	2193	2198	2203	2208	2213	2218	2223	2228	2234	1	1	2	2	3	3	4	4	5
·35	2239	2244	2249	2254	2259	2265	2270	2275	2280	2286	1	1	2	2	3	3	4	4	5
·36	2291	2296	2301	2307	2312	2317	2323	2328	2333	2339	1	1	2	2	3	3	4	4	5
·37	2344	2350	2355	2360	2366	2371	2377	2382	2388	2393	1	1	2	2	3	3	4	4	5
·38	2399	2404	2410	2415	2421	2427	2432	2438	2443	2449	1	1	2	2	3	3	4	5	5
·39	2455	2460	2466	2472	2477	2483	2489	2495	2500	2506	1	1	2	2	3	3	4	5	5
·40	2512	2518	2523	2529	2535	2541	2547	2553	2559	2564	1	1	2	2	3	3	4	5	5
·41	2570	2576	2582	2588	2594	2600	2606	2612	2618	2624	1	1	2	2	3	4	4	5	5
·42	2630	2636	2642	2648	2655	2661	2667	2673	2679	2685	1	1	2	2	3	4	4	5	6
·43	2692	2698	2704	2710	2716	2723	2729	2735	2742	2748	1	1	2	2	3	4	4	5	6
·44	2754	2761	2767	2773	2780	2786	2793	2799	2805	2812	1	1	2	3	3	4	4	5	6
·45	2818	2825	2831	2838	2844	2851	2858	2864	2871	2877	1	1	2	3	3	4	5	5	6
·46	2884	2891	2897	2904	2911	2917	2924	2931	2938	2944	1	1	2	3	3	4	5	5	6
·47	2951	2958	2965	2972	2979	2985	2992	2999	3006	3013	1	1	2	3	3	4	5	6	6
·48	3020	3027	3034	3041	3048	3055	3062	3069	3076	3083	1	1	2	3	4	4	5	6	6
·49	3090	3097	3105	3112	3119	3126	3133	3141	3148	3155	1	1	2	3	4	4	5	6	7
	0	1	2	3	4	5	6	7	8	9	1	2	3	4	5	6	7	8	9

ANTI-LOGARITHMS

	0	1	2	3	4	5	6	7	8	9	1	2	3	4	5	6	7	8	9
·50	3162	3170	3177	3184	3192	3199	3206	3214	3821	3228	1	1	2	3	4	4	5	6	7
·51	3236	3243	3251	3258	3266	3273	3281	3289	3296	3304	1	2	2	3	4	5	5	6	7
·52	3311	3319	3327	3334	3342	3350	3357	3365	3373	3381	1	2	2	3	4	5	5	6	7
·53	3388	3396	3404	3412	3420	3428	3436	3443	3451	3459	1	2	2	3	4	5	6	6	7
·54	3467	3475	3483	3491	3499	3508	3516	3524	3532	3540	1	2	2	3	4	5	6	6	7
·55	3548	3556	3565	3573	3581	3589	3597	3606	3614	3622	1	2	2	3	4	5	6	7	7
·56	3631	3639	3648	3656	3664	3673	3681	3690	3698	3707	1	2	3	3	4	5	6	7	8
·57	3715	3724	3733	3741	3750	3758	3 767	3776	3784	3793	1	2	3	3	4	5	6	7	8
·58	3802	3811	3819	3828	3837	3846	3855	3864	3873	3882	1	2	3	4	4	5	6	7	8
·59	3890	3899	3908	3917	3926	3936	3945	3954	3963	3972	1	2	3	4	5	5	6	7	8
·60	3981	3990	3999	4009	4018	4027	4036	4046	4055	4064	1	2	3	4	5	6	7	7	8
·61	4074	4083	4093	4102	4111	4121	4130	4140	4150	4159	1	2	3	4	5	6	7	8	9
·62	4169	4178	4188	4198	4207	4217	4227	4236	4246	4256	1	2	3	4	5	6	7	8	9
·63	4266	4276	4285	4295	4305	4315	4325	4335	4345	4355	1	2	3	4	5	6	7	8	9
·64	4365	4375	4385	4395	4406	4416	4426	4436	4446	4457	1	2	3	4	5	6	7	8	9
·65	4467	4477	4487	4498	4508	4519	4529	4539	4550	4560	1	2	3	4	5	6	7	8	9
·66	4571	4581	4592	4603	4613	4624	4634	4645	4656	4667	1	2	3	4	5	6	7	8	10
·67	4677	4688	4699	4710	4721	4732	4742	4753	4764	4775	1	2	3	4	5	7	8	9	10
·68	4786	4797	4808	4819	4831	4842	4853	4864	4875	4887	1	2	3	4	6	7	8	9	10
·69	4898	4909	4920	4932	4943	4955	4966	4977	4989	5000	1	2	3	5	6	7	8	9	10
·70	5012	5023	5035	5047	5058	5070	5082	5093	5105	5117	1	2	4	5	6	7	8	9	11
·71	5129	5140	5152	5164	5176	5188	5200	5212	5224	5236	1	2	4	5	6	7	8	10	11
·72	5248	5260	5272	5284	5297	5309	5321	5333	5346	5358	1	2	4	5	6	7	9	10	11
·73	5370	5383	5395	5408	5420	5433	5445	5458	5470	5483	1	3	4	5	6	8	9	10	11
·74	5495	5508	5521	5534	5546	5559	5572	5585	5598	5610	1	3	4	5	6	8	9	10	12
·75	5623	5636	5649	5662	5675	5689	5702	5715	5728	5741	1	3	4	5	7	8	9	10	12
·76	5754	5768	5781	5794	5808	5821	5834	5848	5861	5875	1	3	4	5	7	8	9	11	12
·77	5888	5902	5916	5929	5943	5957	5970	5984	5998	6012	1	3	4	6	7	8	10	11	12
·78	6026	6039	6053	6067	6081	6095	6109	6124	6138	6152	1	3	4	6	7	8	10	11	13
·79	6166	6180	6194	6209	6223	6237	6252	6266	6281	6295	1	3	4	6	7	9	10	12	13
·80	6310	6324	6339	6353	6368	6383	6397	6412	6427	6442	1	3	4	6	7	9	10	12	13
·81	6457	6471	6486	6501	6516	6531	6546	6561	6577	6592	2	3	5	6	8	9	11	12	14
·82	6607	6622	6637	6653	6668	6683	6699	6714	6730	6745	2	3	5	6	8	9	11	12	14
·83	6761	6776	6792	6808	6823	6839	6855	6871	6887	6902	2	3	5	6	8	9	11	13	14
·84	6918	6934	6950	6966	6982	6998	7015	7031	7047	7063	2	3	5	6	8	10	11	13	14
·85	7079	7096	7112	7129	7145	7161	7178	7194	7211	7228	2	3	5	7	8	10	12	13	15
·86	7244	7261	7278	7295	7311	7328	7345	7362	7379	7396	2	3	5	7	8	10	12	14	15
·87	7413	7430	7447	7464	7482	7499	7516	7534	7551	7568	2	3	5	7	9	10	12	14	16
·88	7586	7603	7621	7638	7656	7674	7691	7709	7727	7745	2	4	5	7	9	11	12	14	16
·89	7762	7780	7798	7816	7834	7852	7870	7889	7907	7925	2	4	5	7	9	11	13	14	16
·90	7943	7962	7980	7998	8017	8035	8054	8072	8091	8110	2	4	6	7	9	11	13	15	17
·91	8128	8147	8166	8185	8204	8222	8241	8260	8279	8299	2	4	6	8	10	11	13	15	17
·92	8318	8337	8356	8375	8395	8414	8433	8453	8472	8492	2	4	6	8	10	12	14	15	17
·93	8511	8531	8551	8570	8590	8610	8630	8650	8670	8690	2	4	6	8	10	12	14	16	18
·94	8710	8730	8750	8770	8790	8810	8831	8851	8872	8892	2	4	6	8	10	12	14	16	18
·95	8913	8933	8954	8974	8995	9016	9036	9057	9078	9099	2	4	6	8	10	12	14	17	19
·96	9120	9141	9162	9183	9204	9226	9247	9268	9290	9311	2	4	6	9	11	13	15	17	19
·97	9333	9354	9376	9397	9419	9441	9462	9484	9506	9528	2	4	7	9	11	13	15	17	20
·98	9550	9572	9594	9616	9638	9661	9683	9705	9727	9750	2	4	7	9	11	13	16	18	20
·99	9772	9795	9817	9840	9863	9886	9908	9931	9954	9977	2	5	7	9	11	14	16	18	21
	0	1	2	3	4	5	6	7	8	9	1	2	3	4	5	6	7	8	9

INDEX